Pain and Gender

Pain and Gender

Gillian Bendelow

An imprint of **Pearson Education**

Harlow, England · London · New York · Reading, Massachusetts · San Francisco · Toronto · Don Mills, Ontario · Sydney
Tokyo · Singapore · Hong Kong · Seoul · Taipei · Cape Town · Madrid · Mexico City · Amsterdam · Munich · Paris · Milan

Pearson Education Ltd
Edinburgh Gate
Harlow
Essex CM20 2JE
England

and Associated Companies around the World.

Visit us on the World Wide Web at:
www.pearsoneduc.com

First published 2000

ISBN 0 582 30777 5

British Library Cataloguing-in-Publication Data
A catalogue record for this book can be obtained from the British Library

Library of Congress Cataloging-in-Publication Data
A catalog record for this book can be obtained from the Library of Congress

10 9 8 7 6 5 4 3 2 1
04 03 02 01 00

Typeset by 35 in 9/13.5 pt Stone Serif
Printed and bound in Great Britain by Henry Ling Ltd., at the Dorset Press,
Dorchester, Dorset

This book is dedicated to Maureen Bendelow 1933–1992

contents

Chapter 7

Conclusions: towards a sociology of pain and gender   *125*

foreword

Both gender and pain are aspects of everyday life, but our experiences of them rarely encapsulate reflections about meaning. Undergoing 'life's lesions' and living as men or women are part of what it means to be human. Clearly, therefore, pain and gender have a lot to do with one another; they are joined at the heart of the human condition.

In this pioneering book, Gillian Bendelow applies a sociological understanding to the intersections between gender and perceptions, definitions and experiences of pain. While a sociological approach to gender is not unusual (the term itself refers to femininity and masculinity as social constructions), most accounts of pain site it unambiguously within medical understandings of the body. The mechanical metaphors driving these understandings have little basis in how people actually experience their bodies, including the vulnerability to unpleasant sensations of various kinds. One of Gill's considerable achievements in this book is to demonstrate how poorly the mind/body divide works as an explanation of certain aspects of human experience. On the contrary, its chief value has been to prop up the hegemonic interests of a set of professional ideologies and practices which have 'owned' our experiences, instead of helping us to understand the meaning of them.

Male stoicism and women's superior coping ability are part of our cultural stereotypes about the experience of pain. Medical sociologists have long puzzled over the basic conundrum thrown up by the statistics of gender and illness; are the health experiences of men and women really different (with the notable exception of reproduction, of course), or do they 'simply' react differently to the same experiences? This question is in an important sense unanswerable because gender and self-perception are so closely intertwined. The people who provided data for Gill's case studies confirm this resistant integrity, at the same time as revealing much more about the role of emotions in the experience and understanding of pain.

Emotions, like the intersections between pain and gender, have been largely ignored by both medical and social scientists (except in the domain of psychotherapy, where they have been studied with a peculiar accultural intensity). It took the arrival of feminist social science in the 1970s to highlight the importance of developing a sociology of emotions that would affirm the significance of this aspect of the human condition, hitherto disregarded as 'feminine'. What is studied and the methods used are connected to who is doing the studying; power and knowledge are intimate bedmates. This pathbreaking attempt to link scientific knowledge about pain and emotions with the everyday experiences of real people, and all of this with our ongoing socialisation as men and women, is part of the rupture in science and knowledge brought about by the politics of feminism. It thus belongs to a body of work that has reshaped both the social and natural sciences, although this is a process that still has a long way to go.

I had the privilege to be personally connected, as Gill's PhD supervisor, with the work that went into this book. Gill was also a founding member of the Social Science Research Unit, which in 1990 split off from the Thomas Coram Research Unit at the Institute of Education to become a separate centre. I think those of us who were in at SSRU's beginnings have very affectionate memories of our pioneering days camping in the attics of 55–9 Gordon Square in Bloomsbury, where we spent far too much time arguing with management about the need for such key resources as rooms, desks, telephones and computers. I sometimes think that the best work is done in difficult circumstances. Of course it is a testable hypothesis that material privilege and scientific productivity are poorly correlated, but the work done by SSRU in those early days certainly had an innovative edge to it.

The first room one encountered when walking up the stairs to SSRU was an extremely small one which housed Gill and her pain study. There was only space for one person in the room, and pinned around the walls were copies of the pictures used in the visual imagery section of her project. Gill also answered the door intercom for us, so I imagine she switched mentally from Munch's *The Sick Child* and Waterhouse's *The Lady of Shalott* to whoever currently wished to gain entry to our attics; and this must have been a far from pain-free experience for her.

It is a tribute to Gill and her persistence that the work got finished and has now materialised in the form of such an interesting and readable book. It goes without saying (but the point of prefaces such as this is to say it) that the book should have an appeal to a very wide audience; all those with a personal or professional interest in pain, including, one hopes, doctors; and students of gender, the emotions and the sociology of health and illness. On the methodological front, the use of visual imagery has a great deal to offer all of us who are tangling with difficult issues about the quality and soundness of 'qualitative' methods.

Having just spent four months in severe pain with a slipped disc, and coping with it not quite as well as I and everyone else expected I ought to, I can also thoroughly recommend this book for making one think in new ways about 'the neglected encounter between pain and meaning'.

Professor Ann Oakley
Social Science Research Unit
University of London

series preface

The New Sociologies Series provides an alternative to the standard texts available. It also provides an insight into the range of contributions that sociologists can make to our understanding of contemporary issues. The Series is, therefore, forward looking and builds upon discussions and debates that open up 'new' fields of social enquiry. Each volume contributes to debates in the discipline and raises issues of relevance to contemporary policy and practice in the twenty-first century.

A hallmark of the Series is the development of theoretically informed empirical work which will be of interest to undergraduate and graduate students of sociology, researchers, scholars and teachers. All together the volumes in the Series will include authored books as well as edited collections that assess and contribute to the development of the discipline.

It is very appropriate that the first volume to be published in the New Sociologies Series comes from Gillian Bendelow who has been a leading exponent of the way in which sociology and sociologists can contribute to our understanding of pain and emotion. This volume deserves a very wide readership within sociology and other social science disciplines as it has the potential to stimulate readers to think about new developments in the discipline and new fields of investigation.

Robert G Burgess
University of Leicester

Series Editor

There is a saying among academics that research is autobiographical; if I had known this when I embarked so enthusiastically into a (later) academic career with a young child to support, I wonder if I would have been quite so highly motivated. This book does not include the numerous jokes in response to the question 'and what do you do?'; men, women and pain is a topic that evokes a multitude of responses.

On a more serious note, pain in the form of 'life's lesions' as Finkler (1994) so eloquently puts it, has been apparent in my life in its broader sense in ways that maybe explain and shape this book. For example:

- The pain of poverty in Africa that my overprivileged colonial childhood took such care to prevent me from seeing.
- The torment of mental illness endured by the rich variety of people I came into contact with as a community psychiatric nurse at the German Hospital, Dalston, London E8.
- The story of my mother who died aged only 58 from cancer of the kidney. Her colourful, exciting, but difficult life resulted in her illness being diagnosed as depression requiring prolonged hospitalisation; the day her tumour was finally discovered she died without ever (officially) knowing that she was indeed medically 'ill' and that her pain was 'real'.

My time as a graduate student at the University of London was tough and challenging, but intellectually and culturally a golden era, during which the Social Science Research Unit was born. I was fortunate to be under the visionary eye of Ann Oakley, who has a rare capacity to both inspire and stretch one to the utmost without being at all undermining, and I believed I could do anything – even tackle one of the most complex of human conditions. Some years later and somewhat humbled, I have learnt just how hard it is to do justice to this topic.

This study is merely one stepping-stone along the route that Patrick Wall and other humanitarian medics, health professionals and social scientists have carved out to allow the voices of those in pain to be heard. Although fighting his own battle against cancer at this time, Patrick is still taking on the medical establishment in his inimitable way, jousting and joking through the recent launch of his latest book *Pain: The Science of Suffering* (1999) and I treasure the opportunity to have discussed this work with him in Kings Cross Road in the early 1990s.

This study could not have taken place without the encouragement of the GPs who allowed me access to their surgery, which must be kept anonymous, and of course all the people who took part, especially the interviewees who welcomed me into their homes. I am grateful to the ESRC for funding my studentship, and little did I guess that I would be putting the final touches to this study thanks to the good grace of Bob Burgess and the departments of Social Policy and Sociology at the University of Warwick.

There have been so many people, friends and family, who have given intellectual inspiration, emotional and practical support and warmth throughout the project, and indeed continue to do so. It is not possible to include everyone but thanks for those London years to Vivien, Mario, Giancarlo and Cristina Cucurru; Archie, Laura and Richard Bendelow; Paul Tyrell; Ann Oakley, Berry Mayall, Sandra Stone; Colin Samson, Tony Yates, Ros Tennyson, Richard Grover; all at the Social Science Research Unit and the London Medical Sociology Group. Also to Simon Williams who has become inextricably linked with pain, embodiment and emotion in our collaborative work. Finally a very special thank you to Robert Fine for his insightful comments on the final manuscript, as well as for allowing himself to become entangled in the web; and to my daughter Tess, who has listened to, engaged with and generally imbibed concepts of health, illness, pain and suffering all of her young life in some form or other, but has remained a total source of pleasure and joy.

G.B.

acknowledgements

We are grateful to the following for permission to reproduce copyright material:

Elsevier Science for an extract from Vrancken's 'Five Models of Pain' in *Social Science and Medicine* Vol 29, no 3 (1989) and Omnigraphics, Inc. for an extract from *A Barefoot Doctor's Manual* by Geographic Health Studies, translated from a manual originally published in 1970 by the Institute of Traditional Chinese Medicine of Human Province.

The American Association for the Advancement of Science for a figure from Melzack and Wall (1965); Design and Artists Copyright Society (DACS) for *The Sick Child* by Edvard Munch © Munch Museum / Munch–Ellingsen Group, BONO, Oslo, DACS, London 2000 and *Melancholy I*, 1896 by Edvard Munch © Munch Museum / Munch-Ellingsen Group, BONO, Oslo, DACS 2000, Photo © Munch Museum (Svein Andersen/Sidsel de Jong) 2000); The Tate Gallery, London for *A Hopeless Dawn* by Frank Bramley and *The Lady of Shalott* by John William Waterhouse; Magnum Photos for *Famine in India 1951* and *Hungary 1947* by Werner Bischof; Van Gogh Museum (Vincent van Gogh Foundation) for *Old man with his head in his hands, 'At eternity's gate'*; The National Gallery, London for *Saint Sebastian* by Gerrit van Honthorst and *Two Followers of Cadmus Devoured by a Dragon* by Cornelis van Haarlem; Mrs Dolores Olmedo Patiño for *The Broken Column* by Frida Kahlo.

Whilst every effort has been made to trace the owners of copyright material, in a few cases this has proved impossible and we take this opportunity to offer our apologies to any copyright holders whose rights we may have unwittingly infringed.

Some of the data and ideas in this research study have been published in the following journals and books:

Bendelow, G. (1993) 'Pain Perceptions, Emotions and Gender', *Sociology of Health and Illness*, 15(3): 273.

Bendelow, G. and Williams, S.J. (1995a) 'Transcending the dualisms: towards a sociology of pain', *Sociology of Health and Illness*, 17(2): 139–65.

Bendelow, G. and Williams, S.J. (1995b) 'Pain and the mind–body dualism: a sociological approach', *Body and Society*, 1(2): 83–102.

Bendelow, G. and Williams, S.J. (1998a) *Emotions in Social Life: Social Theories and Contemporary Issues*, London: Routledge.

Bendelow, G. and Williams, S.J. (1998b) 'Natural for women, abnormal for men' in S. Nettleton and J. Watson (eds) *The Body in Everyday Life*, London: Routledge.

Williams, S.J. and Bendelow, G. (1998a) *The Lived Body: Sociological Themes, Embodied Issues*, London: Routledge.

Theories of pain

The study of pain has, until very recently, received scant sociological attention despite its critical positioning at the intersection between biology and culture. Theoretical approaches to pain have tended to be dominated by biomedicine and biopsychology, and have concentrated upon its neuro-physiological aspects, both in diagnosis and treatment. Scientific medicine stands accused of reducing the experience of pain to an elaborate broad-casting system of signals, rather than seeing it as moulded and shaped both by individuals and their sociocultural context (see Morris 1991, Good *et al.* 1992, Bendelow 1993, Bendelow and Williams 1995a&b, 1998). It has been argued that a major impediment to a more adequate conceptualisation of pain has been the manner in which it has been 'medicalised', result-ing in the inevitable Cartesian split between body and mind, one of the prime characteristics of the 'medical model'. Consequently, the dominant conceptualisation of pain has focused upon sensation, with the inference that it is able to be rationally and objectively measured. Yet as well as being a medical 'problem', pain is an everyday experience and, while the medical voice is a valid one, other voices, especially those of the subject, are often lost in what Morris calls 'the neglected encounter between pain and meaning' (Morris 1991: 3). This theoretical approach to pain is located within larger debates around medicalisation, the basic argument being that although the benefits and gains from the progress and advancements of scientific medicine are duly acknowledged, these were made at some con-siderable cost to our understanding of the cultural, contextual and social aspects of medicine. In contemporary sociology in the latter half of the

20th century, the claims and assumptions of biomedicine have increasingly been scrutinised and challenged, and medical sociology as a discipline has begun to 'find itself', to occupy a particular place in the radical critique of biomedicine which seeks to restore human perspectives. It is in the wider context of this 'radical' critique of biomedicine that theories of pain are addressed and developed in this study, and which this introduction sets out.

Medicalisation theory and the challenge to biomedicine

The development of a biologically deterministic model of health and illness is historically linked with the rise of the medical profession, and 'medicalisation', in turn, is a strand in the nature/nurture debates which centre on the interaction between biological and cultural determinisms.

Historians of medicine show that the notion of 'disease' can be traced back to Hippocrates, with the postulation that a combination of signs and symptoms can be observed to occur together so frequently and so characteristically as to constitute a recognisable and typical clinical picture. This model was highly influential in the philosophy of René Descartes in the seventeenth century, which has (undeservedly perhaps) been held up in the radical critique as the pinpoint in time when things really began to go wrong. Descartes (1664/1972) saw the mind as activating the will of the human spirit through the subordinate physical matter of the body, a view in opposition to the predominant theological stance of orthodox Christianity on the inseparability of body and soul, which had retarded the development of medical science by forbidding dissection. As well as the revolutionary implications for anatomical study, the philosophical reflections of Descartes did, of course, have a profound influence on the development of positivist science. Logical thought based on empirical observation was emphasised, laying the foundations of the mechanistic biomedical approach, characteristic of what is termed 'Western', 'modern' or 'bio'medicine. Dr Marsden Wagner, a physician with the World Health Organization, lamented in *The Lancet* how pre-seventeenth-century medical care used to combine art and technology at a ratio he estimated at 9:1, until medicine became attached to what he describes as 'the rising star of science and classical mechanical physics' (1982: 1207). According to Wagner, theoretical dichotomies, rooted in ancient Greek philosophy, were given added weight by Descartes, who

at the beginning of the modern era, argued persuasively that the only
path to knowledge was the scientific side of the dichotomy and that
we must ignore or control the artistic side. This one-sided mechanistic
view was applied to medicine, and the body and disease processes
came to be seen in those terms.

(Wagner 1982: 1207)

While the advancement of medical knowledge undoubtedly bene-
fited enormously from the profound insights of Descartes, the radical
critique argues that the Cartesian 'revolution' has limited the scope of
medicine (Turner 1992; Morris 1991, 1998), and indeed in some of the
postmodern feminist writings, verge upon a kind of 'demonisation' dualism (see, for example, Bordo 1986). The philosopher Gilbert Ryle (1949)
pre-empted this whole critical tradition when he emphasised the dangers
and limitations of proposing two collateral but separate histories – those
of the mind and the body. Although it is important to make the distinction between Descartes' own work and the way in which medicine
crudely appropriated aspects of his theory, this book rests on the assumption that Cartesian dualism, translated into a reductionist split between
mind and body, has become one of the major characteristics of the biomedical model, and is one of its most heavily criticised features.

A striking example of how the dominance of this model of health
and illness resonates in practical as well as conceptual implications is
demonstrated in Figure 1 by the extracts from two medical textbooks, one
British and one translated from Chinese from the same period of time
in the 1970s.

Without wishing to idealise the holistic approach (itself subject to
critical scrutiny; see, for instance, Coward 1989 and Armstrong 1995), the
extract from *The Barefoot Doctor's Manual* shows how the mechanistic model
is unable systematically to take a more sophisticated aetiology on board,
overpoliticisation notwithstanding. Other major features of the biomedical model include an orientation towards *cure*, towards the manipulation
of organic symptoms with the intention of effecting their disappearance;
its perception of *disease* as an autonomous and potentially manageable entity
which threatens personal health in a temporary or episodic fashion; its
focus on the isolated *individual* as the site of the disease and as the appropriate object of treatment; and a belief that the most appropriate place for
treatment is a *medical environment* – the consulting room or the hospital
– rather than the environment where symptoms arise.

From another standpoint, the claims of biomedical progress have
been shown to be highly exaggerated from within medicine itself, as in

Figure 1: Comparative East/West medical texts.

In a traditional medical textbook prepared for nurses, and under the heading of aetiology, a rather narrow conception of the causes of disease is given, as follows (Bloom: 1979: 8–9).

The term aetiology is used to denote causation of disease. There are thousands of possible causes and the following classification gives only the main ones:

1. LIVING ORGANISMS OR MICROBES
    a) Bacteria
    b) Viruses
    c) Fungi
    d) Parasites
2. PHYSICAL AND CHEMICAL AGENTS
    a) Injury (trauma)
    b) Excesses of heat or cold
    c) Electricity, X-rays and radioactive substances
    d) Toxic drugs
    e) Poisonous gases
    f) Cigarette smoking
3. DEFICIENCY AND HORMONAL DISEASES
    Lack of disturbance of:
    a) Vitamins
    b) Hormones
    c) Diet
4. HEREDITY
5. AUTOIMMUNE DISEASES
6. UNKNOWN (including causes of tumours).

In contrast, the following extract from *A Barefoot Doctor's Manual*, prepared by the Revolutionary Health Committee of Hunan Province (1978), demonstrates how, in Chinese medicine, emotional and external factors are seen as intrinsic to disease:

HOW TO ANALYZE CAUSES OF DISEASE

To find the cause of disease, on the basis of the patient's signs and symptoms and the physical examination results, is an important step in the diagnosis of the disease. After physicians have gained a certain recognition of disease by the examination techniques just described, they must, in order to understand and make a correct diagnosis, make an overall study of the patient's attitudes, mental activity and illness to correctly differentiate between the aetiology and the present course of the disease. The human body is an integral mechanism in which inconsistencies contradict each other. It also has a very close relationship with society and its natural environment. The onset and development of disease frequently are related to the body's make-up, its resistance

Figure 1:   (contd)

and the virulence and number of pathogens present, in a complex relationship.
The following sections list some causes of disease in the human body; the important
ones refer to mental activity and the physical make-up of the human being:

BODY FACTORS

1. Nervous and Emotional Make-Up
Mental and emotional activity among different individuals vary under the different
influences of society and the natural environment. Examples are joy, excitement,
happiness, anger, fright and sorrow. Under most conditions, emotional activity will
not cause disease, but under certain conditions it can damage normal body function
and cause or hasten its development, e.g. certain neuroses or functional digestive
disturbances. However, we must feel the dynamic effect of the proletarian world view
and its revolutionary optimism on preventing or overwhelming disease. For example,
some of our comrades who have incurred serious burns, because they can hold on to
a fearless revolutionary determination to fight against disease, ultimately overcome it.
This fully explains the dynamic the patient's subjective outlook can have on
overcoming a serious illness.

2. Body Make-Up or Physical Conditions
This includes the body build, body reactions and differences such as age, sex, resistance
to disease, which are closely related to the incurrence and development of disease.
After 1950, the large working masses were given regular training so their bodies may
become healthy and strong, and less susceptible to disease. Furthermore, the aged or
the young, because of a weak body make-up, may, because of weak resistance, be
easily affected by disease-causing factors to become ill. The human body's reactions
to external environmental and internal body factors may vary because of regional,
age, sex and sensitivity difference. For example, children can easily be affected by
infantile paralysis, while older adults are more susceptible to cancer. Some people are
allergic to pollen, shrimp and crab, and develop wheezing or urticaria. Certain other
ailments are commonly seen in men, and others more commonly seen in females.
These are all closely related to the human body's reaction.

EXTERNAL FACTORS

These include various social and natural environmental factors. Sometimes etiologic
factors are quite complex.

SOCIAL FACTORS

Differences in the social system often have a great effect on the incidence and
elimination of certain diseases. China has early eliminated cholera, smallpox, venereal
disease, plague, etc. With respect to certain diseases with more serious consequences

Figure 1: (contd)

---

such as malaria and schistosomiasis, better prevention and treatment measures have greatly reduced the disease incidence. Therefore, when causes of disease are analysed, great emphasis must be given to the social system.

PHYSICAL FACTORS

e.g. Radiation, mechanical injuries, war injuries, high altitude, high temperature, outer space activity etc.

CHEMICAL FACTORS

e.g. Strong acids and alkalis, pharmaceuticals, cyanide products, organic phosphorous in agricultural insecticides and snake venom.

BIOLOGICAL FACTORS

e.g. Pathogenic viruses, bacteria, fungi, spirochetes, protozoa, tapeworms etc. Biological pathogens attacking the human body are quite selective in their site of attack.

CLIMATIC FACTORS

Under normal conditions, natural climatic factors, such as wind, cold, heat, humidity, aridity etc. do not cause disease but if the climate changes suddenly and the body's resistance is lowered and cannot adapt immediately, the above elements are linked to certain symptoms in traditional Chinese medicine.

OTHER FACTORS

e.g. Unhygienic eating habits that lack discipline and control, can also be indirect pathological factors.

(Revolutionary Health Committee of Hunan Province 1978: 25–6)

---

the work of McKeown (1977) which presents scientific evidence to show that infectious disease declined as a result of improvements in public health, but the radical critique is heavily sociological. Interest in how far physical or psychiatric disorder may be a result of living in a particular form of economic and political organisation or domestic environment can be traced back to Marx's and Engels' concern with the social effects of capitalism on the working class, and with the links between these and individual health and well-being. While recognising the potential in terms of progress and civilisation of the (then embryonic) new economic system, Marx and Engels saw the damage to the health and well-being of workers and the *alienation* which the result of inevitable class exploitation would produce:

Within the capitalist system all methods for raising the social productiveness of labour are brought about at the cost of the individual labourer; all means for the development transform themselves into means of domination over, and exploitation of, the producers; they mutilate the labourer into a fragment of a man, degrade him to the level of an appendage to a machine, destroy every remnant of charm in his work, and turn it into hated toil; they estrange him from the intellectual potentialities of the labour process in the same proportion as science is incorporated in it as an independent power; they distort the conditions under which he works, subject him during the labour process to a despotism the more hateful for its meanness, they drag his wife and child beneath the wheels of the juggernaut of capital.   (Marx 1867/1978: 708)

Despite fundamental differences in his conceptions of society, similar concerns can be found in the works of Durkheim, most famously in *Suicide* (1897), and his concept of *anomie* which he used to identify the social causes of high suicide rates in certain social groups.

Marxist analyses of health have formed a major part of the critique viewing medical knowledge as largely determined by the bourgeois ideology of capitalism which erodes social relationships based on kinship, neighbourhood and community (Navarro 1980, Hart 1985). Additionally, there is an 'exportation' of ill health to underdeveloped countries by various means such as the hazards of industrial processes and the dominance of Western scientific medicine, which detracts attention from the basic social and environmental aspects of health (Doyal and Pennell 1979).

Medicalisation theory has argued that the acceptance of a multi-causal model of health and illness by the medical profession has resulted in an increasing medical expansion into numerous areas of life that were previously outside medicine's sphere of influence (Zola 1977; Strong 1979) and that medicine's claim to expertise is bound up with its rise to professional status. During the course of the twentieth century the medical profession has increased its role, prestige and power, by extending into areas such as psychiatry, obstetrics and reproductive health, ageing and even the 'beauty business' on the basis of claims to 'scientific' expertise. That medicine itself was increasingly becoming an institution of social control is illustrated in Friedson's classic statement: 'the medical profession has first claim to jurisdiction over the label of illness and anything to which it may be attached, irrespective of its capacity to deal with it effectively' (1970: 212). A more belligerent critique was developed by Illich (1976) within the ethos of anti-institutionalism expressed in the de-schooling movement with claims that the medical profession has not only misled the public into believing it has a unique, viable and irreplaceable body of knowledge and skills, but has also created a dependence on doctors and medicine which has denigrated people's ability to engage in self-care. He terms this a 'structurally health-denying effect' which results in *iatrogenesis*; thus medical intervention can be regarded as a potential threat to health, with an increasing dependence on science and technology at the expense of spontaneous human capacities to control and shape individual destiny.

Feminist analyses have contributed a great deal to the critique of medicine as a form of social control. Research into childbirth and reproduction (see Oakley 1980, 1984, 1992; Roberts 1981, 1985; Martin 1987) has questioned the benefits allegedly resulting from the take-over by the largely male discipline of obstetrics, and has suggested instead that there may be a reinforcement of women's secondary social status by manipulation of their biology. The attitudes and practices of the medical profession were shown to reflect the dominant interests of men, with women being measured against the male standard of 'normality', and the central determining characteristic of women being seen as their 'natural role to reproduce'. Social control has also been at the centre of anti-racist and disability debates in medicine which are an emergent part of the radical critique (see Ahmad 1993; Kelleher and Hillier 1996; Oliver 1996).

The medicalisation thesis was also central to the critique of social constructionism, which gained so much theoretical ground from the 1970s onwards. In his 'pre-Foucauldian' discussion of illness, Sedgwick (1973) argued that the notion of disease is entirely human and is applied on the basis of social and personal values which can, and do, change. He cites examples such as hookworms being a normal part of health in certain areas of North Africa, and emphasises that any diagnosis of pathology embodies a degree of relativity. He also re-evokes the nature/nurture argument by stressing the inevitability of human decay, giving examples such as a fractured femur in a septuagenarian being as natural as 'the snapping of an autumn leaf from its twig', and infection by cholera as carrying with it 'no more the stamp of illness than the souring of milk by other forms of bacteria' (Sedgwick 1973: 45). But it is the work of Foucault, in particular his analysis of the history of medical theories in France (*The Birth of the Clinic*, 1973), that has been one of the most theoretically influential within medical sociology and the sociology of health and illness (see, for example, Turner 1992, 1995; Armstrong 1983, 1984, 1995; Petersen and Bunton 1997). Foucault's 'political anatomy' is based on mechanisms of power rather than progressive enlightenment or random effect; his 'clinical gaze' demonstrates how changing ideologies of disease can be seen as a product of differing perceptions of the body:

> Disease is no longer a bundle of characters dissociated here and there over the surface of a body and linked together by statistically observable concomitances and successions; it is a set of forms and deformations, figures and accidents, and of displaced, destroyed or modified elements bound together in sequence according to a geography which can be followed step by step. It is no longer a pathological species inserting itself into the body whenever possible; it is the body itself which becomes ill.   (Foucault 1973: 136)

The 'biopolitics' of Foucault has resulted in an unprecedented sociological interest in embodiment which adds weight to the challenge to find a *rapprochement* between social and biological models of health and illness. While biomedical research will continue to be vital, it is also important to advance understanding of the social and socioeconomic factors that play a part in the promotion of health and the causation of disease, and of the relationship between these and the broader social structure. Instead of remaining embedded in debates between biological and cultural determinism, the position adopted in this book is that the way forward involves an integrated understanding of the relationship between the biological and the social.

Sociological approaches to pain

Although this book is trying to develop a *sociology* of pain, it recognises the role of psychology, psychiatry, philosophy and anthropology as well as the enormous paradigm shifts that have taken place within medicine itself over the latter half of this century. The advances that have been made in pain relief are a tribute to the humanitarian efforts of those individuals such as Dame Cicely Saunders, Patrick Wall and John Bonica. In this tradition this book is not concerned with rejecting or 'rubbishing' medicine but argues more modestly that the contribution of sociology and phenomenology enhances our understanding of pain, and that narrative accounts, as Trisha Greenhalgh (1998: 247) points out, have their place firmly alongside evidence-based medicine. In other words, the argument as such is with the rigidity and limitations of the self-understandings of biomedicine, and what is being claimed here is that sociological and phenomenological approaches to pain contribute to the formation of, and enhance greatly, new holistic paradigms in the study of pain.

This book is based upon empirical research which reveals how pain is conceptualised beyond mere sensations, and is akin to what have been aptly described as 'life's lesions':

> The concept of life's lesions recognises that human infirmities cannot be reduced to one or two factors alone. These lesions are fluid; they sum up multiple causes that are fostered by and rise out of perceived adversity, hostile social relations, stressful life events, or unresolved contradictions that corrode one's existence, take hold of the body, and carve impairments upon it. Life's lesions express through the body deleterious conditions of existence, be they poverty, malnutrition, adverse life events, perceived discrepancies in our culturally shaped image of ourselves and attributes of our body, or other unreconcilable contradictions.
> (Finkler 1994: 16)

There is an emphasis here on the meaning and 'lay' understanding of the phenomena of pain which has been reflected in recent developments in the sociology of health and illness, and in the area of emotions and embodiment. In turn, the emphasis on understanding emotions and feelings bridges the mind/body divide which characterises the more traditional psychophysical and biomedical approaches.

In this study, a multi-method form of enquiry was adopted, including a self-completing questionnaire administered to a random sample of 107 men and women attending a GP practice in North West London, followed by an in-depth interview with a self-selecting sub-sample which included a sequence of visual imagery. Significant gender differences were found in the significance of both the role of the emotions and the role of social expectations, in that women were believed to have superior coping capacities. These themes were explored further in the qualitative fieldwork, and demonstrated the vulnerable feelings and the existential or religious beliefs that experiences of pain incorporate, as well the sensory components. The attribution to women, by both sexes, of superior capacities in coping with pain are linked to their biological and reproductive functioning, but are underpinned by cultural expectations of roles and socialisation. The 'findings' of the study reflect the particular experiences of people living in a multi-ethnic inner-city area, and, at a more general level, provide a basis for developing new approaches to the understanding of the relationship of pain to cultural, social and emotional life, in particular in relation to gender and embodiment.

chapter 1

Biomedicine and pain

Illness is the doctor to whom we pay most heed; to kindness, to knowledge, we make promises only: pain we obey.

(Proust, *Remembrance of Things Past*)

Debates about the nature of pain have taken place since antiquity. Pain as an emotional experience, the obverse of pleasure, is in fact a much older conceptualisation than of pain as a purely physical sensation. The pain/pleasure dichotomy developed by Aristotle is constantly evoked and reinforced throughout the history of social thought, and pain as an intrinsic feature of the human condition has been one of the most profound philosophical deliberations in the works of Kant, Hume, Tiliich, Kierkegaard, Wittgenstein and Montaigne:

Our well-being is only freedom from pain. That is why the philosophical school which has given the greatest importance to pleasure has also reduced it to the mere absence of pain. Not to suffer is the greatest good man can hope for . . .

(de Montaigne 1592/1959: 44)

From within both medicine and social science, there is an emerging literature which provides an historical and epistemological critique of the 'appropriation' of pain by biomedicine. Since the seventeenth century, theories of pain have been dominated by the rise of scientific medicine and concentrate almost exclusively on the neurophysiological aspects (Wall and Melzack 1984, 1988; Good *et al.* 1992; Morris 1991, 1998) and specifically on what Morris terms 'the vast cultural shift which centres on the eradication of meaning by late nineteenth century science' (1998: 34).

Far from being a one-dimensional physiological process, it is argued within this literature that pain is a complex, multi-layered phenomenon, as Wittgenstein in *Tractacus Logicophilosophicus* (1921/1962) relates. In trying to decipher his recording of the word *empfiding* (toothache) continuously over several days in his diary, he questions his ability to recall the severity of the pain and whether it can be considered to be of the same quality each time it was recorded. Thus the association of pain with memory, with emotion and with language makes its definition a fundamental dilemma, as its etymological definition reveals:

> Pain [from Latin **poena**, meaning penalty]: 1. An unpleasant feeling caused by injury or disease of the body. 2. Mental suffering. 3. [old use] punishment, e.g. on pain of death.
>
> (*Oxford Reference Dictionary*)

Similarly, Procacci and Maresca discuss how, in Greek, the word used most often for physical pain is αλγος (algos) which derives from roots indicating neglect of love (1985: 201). Another Greek word is αχος (achos), meaning 'psychic pain' from which we derive the English 'ache'. Implicit in these meanings is a broader definition of pain than the narrowly defined Cartesian proposition which inevitably acts to divorce mental from physical states and tends to attribute single symptoms to single causes.

Biomedicine and pain

Just as we have seen how the critique of biomedicine has resulted in paradigm shifts in the latter half of this century, it is possible to trace the same story through traditional medico-psychological theories of pain. As late as 1989 John Bonica pointed out that there was no pain curriculum in medical training and the dominant theory, as described in most textbooks of neurophysiology, neurology and neurosurgery and taught to medical students largely as fact, is known as *specificity theory*. The proposition is presented as a straightforward one, and was first classically described by Descartes in 1664: a specific pain system carries messages from pain receptors in the skin to a pain centre in the brain, as shown in Figure 2.

Melzack and Wall (1988: 150) describe how the specificity theory underwent little change until the nineteenth century when, with the emergence of physiology as an experimental science, Muller's theory of specific nerve energies in 1842 contributed an understanding of the sensory processes that relay information to the brain, and, in particular, of the differing qualities of sensation. However, it was assumed that there was a straight-through

Figure 2:   Descartes' illustration of the pain pathway (1664).

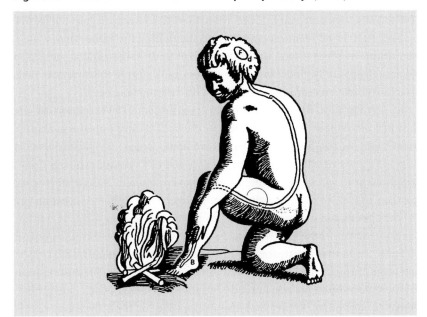

system from the sensory organs (of taste, smell, sight, hearing and touch) to the brain centre responsible for the sensation. An eminent neurosurgeon of the time actually proposed that if the auditory nerve could be connected to the visual cortex, and the visual nerve to the auditory cortex, we would be able to see thunder and hear lightning (Boring 1942). During 1894–5, the physician Max von Frey published a series of articles in which he proposed a theory of the cutaneous senses. He expanded Muller's concept of a single sense of touch to four major cutaneous modalities – touch, warmth, cold and pain – each with its own special projection system to a brain centre responsible for the appropriate sensation.

This theory was expanded during the next fifty years to form the basis of modern-day specificity theory, with separation of modality being extended to peripheral nerve fibres. Eventually a search was made for a 'pain pathway' in the spinal cord (Keele 1957), which was thought to be within the spinothalamic tract ascending in the anterolateral quadrant of the spinal cord. The location of the 'pain centre' was still a source of debate; its location was proposed by Head (1920) as being in the thalamus, with the cortex being assumed to exert inhibitory control over it.

Melzack and Wall (1988) describe how, at the turn of the century, a furious battle raged between the neurologists von Frey and Goldscheider over physiological aspects of pain specificity. Another viewpoint was put forward by H.R. Marshall, the philosopher and psychologist: 'a plague on both your houses; pain is a quale,[1] that colours all sensory events' (Marshall 1894: 167). Marshall maintained that there is a strong negative affective quality that drives us into activity associated with pain, rather than a mere sensation. In other words, we are compelled to do something about it and to act effectively in order to relieve it, beyond a simple reflex action. This places the affective processes parallel with sensory processes.

Throughout the early twentieth century, the development of the hospice movement has contributed to the broadening out of concepts of pain.[2] One of the founders of the movement, Dame Cicely Saunders, in 'Care of the dying' (1976), advocated the notion of *total* pain, which includes psychological, spiritual, interpersonal and even financial aspects of chronic pain, as well as its physical aspects. Another germinal influence contributing to changes in the conceptualisation of pain has been the work of Bonica, an anaesthetist in the United States, who recommended in *The Management of Pain* (1953) that the treatment and understanding of pain would be best achieved through the cooperation of different disciplines. The culmination of these developments was Ronald Melzack and Patrick Wall's radical challenge to specificity theory and the elaboration of their own *gate-control* theory of pain (1965, 1984; Wall and Melzack 1988) – see Figure 3. Wall and Melzack (1984) claim that there are many implicit physiological, anatomical or psychological assumptions in specificity theory, which fail to provide answers to the following observations:

1.   The relationship between injury and pain is highly variable.

2.   Innocuous stimuli may produce pain.

3.   The location of pain may be different from the location of damage.

4.   Pain may persist in the absence of injury after healing.

5.   The nature and location of pain changes with time.

6.   Pain is not a single sensation but has many dimensions.

7.   There is no adequate treatment for certain types of pain, especially idiopathic pains in which there is no sign of tissue damage and no agreed cause (such as low back pains and migraines).

Whereas physiological specialisation for pain sensations can be identified, in that neurons in the nervous system are specialised to conduct patterns of nerve impulses that can be recorded and displayed, psychological specificity cannot be demonstrated in the same way. No neurons in the

---

1.   Meaning emotional quality.
2.   For an account of its history and development, see Mann 1988.

Figure 3:   Melzack and Wall's gate-control theory.

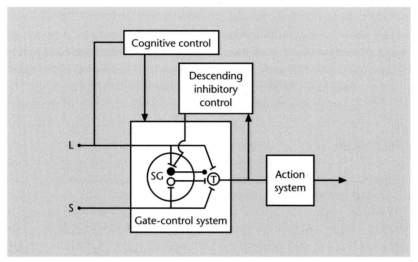

Reprinted with permission from Melzack, R. and Wall, P. 'Pain Mechanisms: a new theory',
Science, **150**. Copyright 1965 American Association for the Advancement of Science.

somatic projection system are indisputably linked to a single, specific psychological experience. Consequently there is no satisfactory definition that
can encompass the diversity of perceptions:

> The word 'pain' represents a category of experiences, signifying a
> multitude of different, unique experiences having different causes, and
> characterised by different qualities varying along a number of sensory,
> affective and evaluative imensions.   (Melzack and Wall 1988: 161)

Melzack and Wall developed and refined the alternative model of
the gate-control theory, which hypothesises that psychological and cognitive variables (heavily influenced by sociocultural learning and experiences)
have an impact on the physiological processes involved in human pain
perception and response. The basis of the gate-control theory is that a
neural mechanism in the dorsal horns area of the spinal cord

> acts like a gate which can increase or decrease the flow of nerve
> impulses from peripheral nerve fibres into the central nervous system.
> Somatic input is therefore subjected to the modulating influence of
> the gate before it evokes pain perception and response.
> (Melzack and Wall 1988: 222)

These gates are proposed to be located in the *substantia gelatinosa*
(SG) of the dorsal horns, where the peripheral nerve fibres enter and are
joined with the central transmission fibres (T) to the brain (see Figure 3).

The degree to which the gate increases or decreases sensory transmission is determined by the relative activity in nerve fibres, and by descending influences from the brain, so that cognitive or higher central nervous system processes such as attention, anxiety, anticipation and past experiences exert a powerful influence on pain processes (Melzack and Wall 1988: 230). Despite widespread discussion of the gate-control theory by researchers, and the conclusions of many that such a theory is useful in addressing formerly puzzling aspects of pain, clinical medicine was slow to challenge the traditional biomedical paradigm which divorces mental from physical states and attempts to attribute single symptoms to single causes.

Psychomedical approaches

The same 'biomedical' story is true of the study of perceptions of pain which lies at the intersection of medicine and social science. Traditionally, social science research in this area is dominated by the field of psychology, particularly psychophysics.

The study of perception within psychology was traditionally concerned with the extraction of perceptual cues from sensory inputs in order to distinguish and convert them into meaningful precepts, heavily embedded in psychophysics, using experimental methods that inflict (often noxious) stimuli on subjects. From the mid-nineteenth century onwards, investigations of psychological responses to physical stimuli were carried out by experimental scientists, attempting to chart the limits of sensation using analogies from physical science, which equated individual sensations with atoms, and from which the extensive body of work on thresholds emerged. A *threshold* is defined as the minimum amount of stimulation to which observers will report they have experienced a sensation. It is measured by the experimenter increasing the intensity of a stimulus, such as a pinpoint of light or touch on the skin, until the observer reports an awareness (Greene 1990). When conducting experiments, it was noted that sometimes the observer would report a sensation and sometimes not. This led to the development of the concept of an absolute threshold, defined as the observer reporting the stimulus on 50 per cent of occasions. The stimulus may be less noticeable under different conditions, or different parts of the body, and the term Just Noticeable Differences (JNDs) indicates distinct different sensations, which may be very close together on sensitive areas, but quite far apart on those less so, for example, the back of the neck. Weber's Law states that the difference in intensity between the two stimuli has to be proportionately the same for a JND to be reported (Greene 1990: 237).

These methods claim to have much success in predicting responses to sensory inputs. The measurement of thresholds has informed the bulk of research on pain perception, which again concentrates on the sensory component or *nociception*, and is based upon the principle of a continuum of sensation which becomes painful to a threshold that is intolerable. *Threshold* refers to the first painful perception of the stimulus, whereas *tolerance* is the point at which the subject reports being unable to tolerate the stimulus any longer (Elton, Stanley and Burrows 1983). The relationship between the two is uncertain, as precise measurements are difficult to obtain, and the Signal Detection Theory (Gregory 1972) acknowledges the existence of a fluctuating amount of background activity in the central nervous system which would give rise to a range of magnitudes of reporting thresholds.

This focus on psychological factors in pain perception has led to many experimental studies, and journals such as the monthly *Pain*, published by Elsevier, are primarily concerned with research of this nature, most of which is clinically controlled trials, involving the infliction of pain on subjects to measure pain threshold and tolerance. Hardy *et al.* (1968) conducted numerous experimental studies of pain perception, concerned mainly with skin temperature. However, wider issues and, in particular, the ethical implications of inflicting pain on subjects in these studies are rarely discussed in these journals, and studies of this nature continue to be carried out to the present day. The experimental nature of these studies does not allow the social context to be taken into account and the psychological research on pain perception is weighted heavily towards sensory cues, with little emphasis on the subjectivity, or indeed any recognition of models of perception that emphasise interaction between sensory cues and expectations or prior experience (Neisser 1976: 214).

With scientific breakthroughs generated by medics like Wall and Melzack, the gate-control theory has been influential in expanding the rather narrow focus on pain tolerance and thresholds, the dominant approach within the study of pain perception. The first pain clinic was set up in the United States in 1961 with specialists from thirteen different disciplines, aiming to collaborate in a non-hierarchical manner. The subsequently developed pain centres throughout North America and Europe vary in provision and resources, but they are characterised by a diversity in the organisation of work, medical specialities, working principles and therapies.

Debates about the contribution of psychology in this multi-disciplinary arena have abounded. Harre and Secord (1972: 2) point out that, although there has been much criticism of 'naive behaviourism', in any clinical practice there remains a generalised adherence to positivist methodology, despite the fact that empirical studies only make sense if people are conceived of in the mechanical tradition as 'passive entities whose behaviour is the product of impressed forces'. They maintain that an adequate social psychology must provide a general theory of social action and genesis, and must be a cooperative enterprise between philosophy, psychology and sociology so that each area can compensate for inadequacies of the other:

> Psychologists are concerned with too narrow a conception of social action, severely handicapped by social naiveté. Philosophers have not lacked conceptual sophistication but too often have been ignorant of social and psychological facts. Sociologists, despite a great breadth of conception, have been unable to develop theories of individual social action, and have suffered from conceptual naiveté.
>
> (Harre and Secord 1972: 2)

The potential for psychology to 'transcend' itself by attempting to understand the social context of its various approaches and traditions has been echoed repeatedly, as in this plea by Buss:

> [to] begin understanding the role of politics, ideologies, values, economic systems, and in general, society and its underlying strategies and dynamics – in the birth, development and death of some of the classical psychological theories, perspectives, paradigms, models or approaches that have and continue to exert considerable influence.
>
> (Buss 1975: 991)

Acknowledging the enormity of this task, Buss identified key issues in the form of antagonistic paradigms such as nature/nurture, behaviourism/ humanism and mechanistic/holistic, and accentuated the value of engaging in debates with greater exposure to a variety of intellectual traditions, value systems and perceptual frames of reference, resulting in an enriched development of the individual.

Although more recent experimental research has begun to encompass questions such as the relationship between the patient's 'mental state' and pain, the use of experimental techniques can result in a process that could be described, at best, to be 'dehumanising' and, at worst, imbued with metaphors of the atrocities perpetrated on humans in the name of 'science' in the Nazi death camps.

The following example describes how evidence was collected to demonstrate the positive relationship between anxiety and pain, often using measures of pain thresholds produced by pain stimulators. Dougher, Goldstein and Leigh (1987), investigating the pain thresholds of eighty undergraduate students, describe how the painful stimulus was produced:

A modified Forgione and Barber (1971) focal pressure pain stimulator
was used. The device consists of a dull lucite knife edge (.6mm thick)
applied at a continuous pressure (1000 g) to the second phalanx of
the participants' fingers. The device produces a dull aching sensation
that gradually builds into a throbbing pain.

(Dougher, Goldstein and Leigh 1987: 260)

The participants were given anxiety-eliciting statements prior to the
stimulus and, unsurprisingly, findings showed that pain-specific anxiety
led to increased perceptions of pain on a seven-point self-reported scale.
The 'experimentees' tend to be university students who receive payment
for their participation and presumably give informed consent to these
practices.

Other studies describe hands being plunged into buckets of iced
water and live electrodes applied to various parts of the body. One paper
in *Pain* recapitulated quite vividly and cheerfully how two (very small)
groups of women were 'artificially' induced to orgasm, and one group
given electric shocks via electrodes inserted into their vaginas in the
process. The findings reported that the women in the nociceptive group
were as 'successful' (*sic*) at reaching orgasm as the control group and concluded that the study demonstrated the links between sexual pleasure
and pain.

Of course, within psychology, there has also been a wealth of less
intrusive and controversial methods such as observations of pain behaviours during physical examination, ratings of pain, measures of activity
and medication level. These measures were used by Keefe (1986) to show
the degree to which depression predicts pain and pain behaviour. The
findings indicate that depression is an important factor that needs to
be considered when evaluating the clinical significance of pain and pain
behaviour in patients with low back pain. In similar vein, Merskey (1965)
argues that hysteria has a strong correlation with pain: in his study, 75 per
cent of patients with heart symptoms caused by anxiety complained of
pain; out of a sample of patients attending gastro-intestinal clinics, 75 per
cent complained of pain, and 38 per cent of those had psychological
disorders without associated evidence of organic disease. He found conver-
sion symptoms of pain associated strongly with neurosis and hysterical
conditions rather than with psychotic illness and brain damage, and the
reported rates of pain were much higher in psychiatric out-patient clinics
than in-patients. Merskey and Spear (1967) evoke the mind/body split
in their definition of the distinction between 'organic' and 'psychogenic'
pain as follows:

Organic pain is 'pain which is largely dependent upon irritation of nerve endings or nerves, or else due to a lesion of the central nervous system, including some possibly patho-physiological disturbances like causalgia'[3]
(Merskey and Spear 1967: 19)

Psychogenic pain is 'either pain which is independent of peripheral stimulation or damage to the nervous system and due to emotional factors, or else pain in which any peripheral change (e.g. muscle tension) is a consequence of emotional factors'
(Merskey and Spear 1967: 19)

Although this distinction may have uses, Elton *et al.* (1983) advised against emphasising it, as they point out that all 'organic' pain has a psychological component and simplistic links between emotional factors and 'psychogenic' pain are inconclusive. For instance, the notion of the pain-prone personality (Engel 1958) has profoundly influenced perceptions of the emotional component of pain. It has also led to the categorisation of pain lacking welldefined physiological causes as 'imaginary' and the *chronic pain syndrome*, a stigmatising condition where pain

fails to heal either naturally or to respond to normal forms of medical intervention [and] becomes difficult and frustrating for both patient and physician. The only effective treatment is seen to be through either a psychiatrist or behaviourally orientated psychologist.
(Soluriac, Cahn and Charpentier 1968)

In true Pavlovian style, pain management or behaviourism is only viewed as possible with the 'well-motivated', by eliminating so-called 'rewards' that have, in the past, resulted from pain behaviours, and substituting what are described as more 'constructive' activities. It is small wonder that the people I interviewed in a pain relief clinic saw themselves as lost causes and described their treatment trajectory as being at the 'end of the line' when they were referred to the pain management clinic (Bendelow 1996). Indeed, one interviewee felt that, from the way he was perceived by health professionals there, he might as well be having 'basket therapy in the loony-bin'.

Generally, the (early and far from exhaustive) psychological literature reviewed has been highly influential upon modern theory but has had a tendency to uphold rather than challenge the biomedical model with inevitable theoretical and methodological limitations, due to the tendencies

---

3. Pain referred to in the distribution of a cutaneous nerve which persists long after an injury to that nerve.

to isolate people from the contexts in which they live,[4] as Maslow's (1987) harsh criticism warns of the limitations of the study of perception within psychology:

> Perception is too much the limited study of mistakes, distortion, illusions and the like. Wertheimer would have called it the study of psychological blindness. What are the factors that make it possible for healthy people to perceive reality more effectively, to predict the future more accurately, to perceive more easily what people are really like, that make it possible for them to endure or to enjoy the unknown, the unstructured and ambiguous and the mysterious? Why do the wishes and hopes of healthy people have so little power to distort their perceptions? The healthier people are, the more their capacities are interrelated. This holds also for the sensory modalities.
>
> (Maslow 1987: 67)

Sociocultural factors

There have been efforts to 'demedicalise' the experience of pain by supplying evidence of the important role that psychological factors play in pain perception and response although the famous war surgeon Beecher was one of the first to stress the impact of the cultural meaning of pain on its perception and response. (He found that injured combat soldiers reported little or no pain associated with their wounds, despite serious tissue trauma (Beecher 1959). Having established that they were actually capable of feeling pain, he also observed that they did not appear to be in shock, and concluded that their perception of pain had been altered by the motivation of being able to return home.)

Medical anthropology extended this analysis considerably with Helman's propositions:

1. Not all social or cultural groups respond to pain in the same way.

2. How people perceive and respond to pain, both in themselves and others, can be largely influenced by their cultural background.

---

4. This is by no means a comprehensive review of clinical psychology and, as a medical sociologist, I realise that I may be guilty of setting up 'straw men' by not including the excellent and enlightened work that takes place in many Pain Clinics, for instance, in the Pain Management Unit at Bath (see Ecclestone 1997) and at the Palliative Care Unit at the Royal Marsden.

3.   How, and whether, people communicate their pain to health
      professionals and to others, can be influenced by cultural factors.
      (Helman 1979: 95)

In order to clarify whether pain is expressed as a symptom or not,
Helman suggests a distinction between private and public pain. Reactions
to pain are not simply involuntary and instinctual, but take place within
a social context, and contain a voluntary component in that action to relieve
pain may or may not be sought, and the help of others enlisted or not
enlisted. Certain cultural or social groups may hold stoicism in esteem, so
that keeping pain private, or expressing it publicly, may be desirable within
a particular social group's major values. Zola's classic study (1966) of
reactions to illness by Italian-Americans and Irish-Americans, using non-
participant observation in the Accident and Emergency Department of a
large New York hospital, is still quoted as the best-known study of the relationship between culture and pain. The Italian response in the study was
identified by Zola as a defence mechanism to cope with anxiety by expres-
siveness and expansiveness, by repeatedly over-expressing it and thereby
dissipating it, whereas the Irish response was to ignore or play down the
symptoms, particularly of pain – a different type of defence mechanism.
A similar study by Zborowski (1952) examined the cultural components
of the experience of pain among Italian-Americans, Jewish-Americans and
largely Protestant 'Old Americans', again revealing marked differences
between the groups. The Italian group was said to lay great emphasis on
the immediacy of experiencing pain, especially on the actual sensation,
but to forget their suffering quickly once it had gone. The Jewish group
was said to be mainly concerned with the meaning and significance of
the pain in relation to their health and welfare – their anxieties were
concentrated on the implications for the future of the pain experience. In
contrast, the 'Old Americans' were described as much less emotional and
more detached in reporting pain, often having an idealised picture of how
to react, and trying to avoid 'being a nuisance'.

Of course, these dated studies reinforce crude ethnic stereotypes,
and as Bates (1987: 48) points out, they can also be criticised for their
failure to control for the influence on pain intensity of other medical,
psychological and sociocultural variables. However, they are important in
initiating a serious sociological approach to understanding pain by taking
into account the social identity of the subject. Central to this process is
the formation of pain beliefs, which are thought to be a major component
in the perception of pain. Williams and Thorn (1989) define pain beliefs
as follows:

A subset of a patient's belief system which represents a personal understanding of the pain experience . . . these beliefs develop through the assimilation of new information (e.g. diagnoses, symptoms, emotional reactions) with pre-existing meaning and action patterns held by the patient.   (Williams and Thorn 1989: 76)

Their work suggests that personal beliefs about affliction may well be discordant with scientific understanding, and vary from representations offered by health professionals. Such discordance may affect compliance with methods of chronic pain treatment. Williams and Thorn developed a Pain Beliefs and Perception Inventory (PBAPI), the use of which revealed three dimensions of pain beliefs, namely self-blame, perception of pain as mysterious, and beliefs about the duration of pain. These were found to be associated with subjective pain intensity, poor self-esteem, somatisation and psychological distress. Suggestion, distraction of attention, evaluation of the meaning of the situation and the feeling of control over potential injury have all been shown to affect physical as well as emotional pain. However, these and other relevant factors also have cultural and sociological components which are given inadequate emphasis. So, it is argued, in order to develop a more sophisticated model of pain, which locates individuals within their social and cultural contexts, a more sociological analysis is needed, not to replace the role of medicine or indeed psychology, but to enhance and add to our overall understanding of the complex phenomena of pain. The next chapter outlines some of these recent approaches which analyse pain in a holistic and socially contextual manner, and considers how sociological approaches contribute to these processes.

chapter 2

Sociological perspectives on pain

Chapter 1 examined some of the major challenges to the dominant biomedical paradigm which have gathered momentum over the latter half of this century. This chapter will consider further some theoretical insights, from within the social sciences generally and from sociology in particular, which underpin the essential framework for this particular study.

'New' paradigms of medicine tend to be more interdisciplinary and holistic, especially as regards some of the more intractable, non-curable chronic conditions which medicine is unable to alleviate, and of which pain, particularly chronic rather than acute pain, is of course a prime example. Developments within the sociology of health and illness over the last two decades, in particular the work around chronic illness and illness narratives,[1] have had a tremendous impact. In parallel, the mind–body divide has been further transcended by sociological deliberations on the role of embodiment and emotion. Of significance also has been the influence of the sociology of gender, especially in relation to the development of qualitative techniques within health and illness. Indeed, it is the methodological implications of all these developments, in particular the use of pain stories and narratives, that are the primary focus of this book. The theoretical constructs of chronic illness, feminist theory, embodiment and emotion are strands that overlap and intertwine with each other, but which have been elaborated upon in much greater detail elsewhere, and are subsequently summarised briefly in this chapter as a backdrop to the study.

---

1. It is impossible to represent adequately here the substantial body of work around illness narratives – see Hydén (1997) for a useful summary.

Chronic illness and illness narratives

The shift over the last decade or so from the sociology of medicine to the sociology of health and illness has political as well as theoretical dimensions in that the discipline sees itself less as upholding and confirming the dominance of medical practice and more as allowing the 'lay' voice to be heard. Nowhere has this been more marked than in the use of illness narrative which, as well as receiving substantial recognition from within sociology and other social sciences, can also be seen to have brought about a paradigm shift within medicine.[2] In his meta-review, Hydén (1997) traces the progression of this work from the early 1980s on biographical disruption (Bury 1982) and narrative reconstruction (Williams 1984) through to the rich tradition of illness narratives into the 1990s (Kleinman 1988; Frank 1995; Good *et al.* 1992) which draw on the philosophising of MacIntyre (1982), Ricoeur (1984) and Taylor (1989) to show how we create our own moral, political and social knowledge bases and world-views to create meaning and make sense of our lives. Hydén makes distinctions about the different ways of using narrative in accounts of illness: illness *as* narrative; narrative *about* illness; narrative *as* illness (1997: 48–69) and Greenhalgh and Hurwitz (1998: 7) indicate the many levels where narrative can be seen as beneficial to medicine: as part of a holistic *therapeutic process*; to provide experiential and reflexive *education* for both patients and professionals; to create a less hierarchical dialogue between clinician and patient, allowing for phenomenological expression of symptoms which in turn give rise to analytical clues and interpretation of meaning within the *diagnostic encounter*; and finally, narrative methods can set a patient-centred *research agenda* which may, in turn, challenge received wisdom and generate new hypotheses.

The narrative approach is central to Kortaba's (1983) existential analysis of the process of becoming a 'pain-afflicted' person. Reconstructions and self-perceptions are used with pain biographies of people who have sought treatment, in order to trace the continuity of personal identity. Kortaba (1983: 243–4) identifies three stages in this process:

---

2. This claim is reflected in the current acclaim for narrative-based medicine which can be found in series in medical journals and in themed medical conferences as well as in the *British Medical Journal* publication (Greenhalgh and Hurwitz 1998).

1. *Onset* – perceived to be transitory, able to be dealt with by diagnosis and treatment. Pain is diagnosed as 'real' by physician, having a physiological basis.

2. *Emergence of doubt* – treatment may not work, increase in specialist consultations, but patient still in control as seeking best care available.

3. *Chronic pain experience* – after shortcomings of treatment, patient may return to lay frame of reference, then the chronic pain subculture.

In the emergence of the 'chronic pain career', two themes emerge – the clinical and the experiential. These themes are echoed in Mishler's (1984) delineation of the two voices in the medical interview – the 'voice of medicine' (biomedical, clinical information) and the 'voice of the lifeworld' (social, contextual information). Although these experiences are not mutually exclusive of each other, there is an implied hierarchy among health professionals in which the former is to be routine and normative, whereas the latter is more likely to be perceived as irrelevant, or even disruptive.

While acknowledging the potential of this approach, Bazanger (1989) also criticised its limits, namely the contextual dimension and the possibility of economic, social and cultural variations, and the risk that in the end the pain defines the person rather than the other way around. In an exploration of the phenomenological approach, she notes how medical sociology has begun to make enquiries into the connotation of 'living with' illness and to concentrate on the *experience* of the sufferer. This restores the illness to the patient, which she claims is a welcome reaction to what she terms as the 'medicocentrism' of theorists such as Parsons and Friedson. Existentiality permeates through therapeutic approaches, for example in the following address rejecting notions of passivity by Carmichael (1985) to a multi-disciplinary audience of therapists working with people in chronic pain:

> Constructive use of pain can only be achieved if we can see the pain as an ally – if we can confront it. The natural response is to express; the social response is to suppress. Fearing it, distancing it, protecting ourselves from it, makes it stronger. The more you push it away, the more it pushes its hooks into you . . . you need to confront it, enter into a dialogue with it, ask it what it's saying to you . . . anger can provide a substitute for pain, but may be used destructively rather than constructively . . . permanent anger is a stuck form of pain. What is useless is denial or avoidance of pain; we need, as Camus advised in *The Plague*, to root ourselves in our distress.   (Carmichael 1985: 9)

Perhaps the most salient role for sociology to play in the understanding of pain is to deconstruct the rigid objectivity of the biomedical model and restore pain to those who experience it; as a discipline, sociology is able to encompass the necessary diversity and flexibility of inquiry and methods and, particularly since the 'Foucauldian revolution', a sociology of pain has begun to emerge. Using Foucault's notion of *le regard*, the medical gaze, to examine the meaning of obstetric pain, Arney and Neill (1982) found a historical change in its conceptualisation: in the pre-war period, pain was one-dimensional and confined to the body, but in the post-war years it developed social and psychological dimensions. Similarly in her analysis of pain in dental practice, Nettleton (1989) stressed the importance of the role of fear, concluding that the movement of pain from the anatomical space to the psychosocial space has resulted in a major conceptual shift which seeks clues and answers in social relationships, rather than in anatomy.

A study of the theory and practice of pain in eight academic pain centres in the Netherlands by Vrancken (1989) identified five broad approaches (see Figure 4).

Integrated multi-disciplinary theories of pain may be more developed in the Netherlands than in Britain and the United States, and it must be acknowledged that the primary role of medicine is to treat and try to alleviate pain. However, as has been pointed out, traditional medical

Figure 4:   Vrancken's five models of pain.

1. The somatico-technical approach to pain
Pragmatic approach, neuro-physiological model. Pain is organic, with much emphasis on classification; time is the only distinction between acute and chronic. Pain patients classified into: those with real pain, psychiatric disorders and malingerers. Therapy consists mainly of surgical procedures to eradicate, block or ease pain, and long-term use of narcotics. The development of secondary psychological complications is seen as second-rate. Patients are cured when 'objective' signs disappear.

2. The dualistic body-orientated approach
Pain is result of organic, psychological and social factors. Nociception (i.e. purely sensory aspect) is the major factor, but other factors affect its final expression; fits with gate-control theory. Although no distinction between body/mind in theory, this does occur in practice – methodological dualism. Pain patients are of three types: chronic benign, chronic malignant and chronic pain syndrome (CPS), differentiated by clinical history. Therapy

Figure 4: (contd)

depends on prevailing components; limits set by patients. Patients cured
when pain is gone.

3. The behaviourist approach
Pain is chronic, intractable, and consists of overt actions which constitute
pain behaviour. Completely separate from acute pain which is mainly
nociceptive and treated by physicians. Pain persistence is dependent
on behavioural changes which are induced, maintained and reinforced
by rewards from environmental factors; therefore treatment is by a
psychologist. Pain patients may have investment or identity in the pain
and/or the coping mechanisms have failed. 'Ideal' patient can be convinced
pain linked to particular situations and willing to cooperate in programme.
Therapy aims to minimise pain behaviour by setting achievable goals,
rehabilitation and resocialisation. Patient recovered when pain behaviour
replaced by effective 'well behaviour'.

4. The phenomenological approach
Pain seen as a complex of reactions and behaviours, triggered as a
physiological self-defence under harmful conditions, but in its course
independent of the initial event – the 'pain function'. Chronic pain is
the result of an interrupted healing process, the pain sufferer is unable to
find a place in the world, is unable to remain an integrated person due
to ongoing pain experiences, so becomes a patient. Pain patients have
a deficient organic life and remain in existential need, are angry and
distanced from their pain. Therapy aims to return the person to human
life by 'awakening' through human encounter. Patient recovered when
emerges through encounter as a 'whole' person again and does not need
doctors to remain healthy.

5. The consciousness approach
Pain is a problem of consciousness, the part of the body that is in pain
has become part of here-and-now awareness, and finally hurt to core of
existence. Pain is incorporated into the meaning of being human. Pain
patients in principle are anyone complaining of pain; in practice anyone
with chronic pain. Therapy not specific, offers conditions for patient to
work on her/his recovery; main prerequisite is possibility of establishing an
interpersonal relationship, may be any form of treatment but preferably
not invasive surgery. Patient recovered either by pain disappearing or by
gaining enough insight to accept and manage. (Adapted from Vrancken
1989: 435–44)

approaches are unable to claim complete expertise over the relief of suffering. By its very nature, pain lies at the intersection of biology and culture and in order to develop a more holistic account, the emotional, psychological, social, existential and spiritual components of its perception must be taken into account. Some problems are unable to be overcome, and this may to some extent be due to the dependence on the dualism of mind and body, which the next section addresses.

Social theories of embodiment and emotion

The relationship between emotionality and illness was vividly expressed in Freud's accounts of the somatic manifestation of emotional distress, and the plea for the recognition of the impact of human emotional states on medical treatment, which is at the heart of a more holistic understanding of pain, is certainly not new. In his book *The Broken Heart: the Medical Consequences of Loneliness* (1977), Lynch presents evidence to demonstrate the links between cardiovascular disease and emotionally distressing life events. He uses medical technology to demonstrate emotional states, for example electro-encephalographic (ECG) patterns showing dramatic improvements when a nurse holds a patient's hand. Lynch (1985) predicted the growth of 'new clinics' in which the process of 'disembodiment' of symptoms will be accelerated by the generalised use of computer graphics, and emphasises the need for a philosophical shift away from the vision of the human body as purely a group of sophisticated mechanisms.

> Clinicians will be required to make a fundamental change in the way they think about the human body. It will no longer be sufficient, for example, to interpret rationally the meaning of various cardiovascular shifts that occur when a patient talks about emotional struggles. Rather, it will also be necessary for clinicians to interpret emotionally and feel the struggles that such bodily codes signify. The social distance built into current ways of looking at the human body – the view of an objective scientist looking at another bodily object that is clearly separate and distinct – will be expanded to include a new type of social connectedness, where two human beings will be able to share commonly felt emotional experiences at their social membrane. In the new clinic, immunization from the emotional experiences of one's fellow man will no longer be seen as either a vital necessity or a particularly virtuous aspect of scientific objectivity. Such detachment will be seen instead as part of a stance that embraces a limited view of

the human body in dialogue with others, as well as a restricted view
of factors beyond bodily mechanics which influence health.

(Lynch 1985: 281)

During some ten years or so since I began this study, areas such
as the sociology of emotion[3] and 'the body'[4] have made their mark on
the theoretical landscape, and much of my own (collaborative) research
has been concerned with developing theoretical models of emotion and
embodiment that transcend mind and body and integrate the biological
and the social (Bendelow and Williams 1995a,b,c, 1998; Williams and
Bendelow 1998a).

Theoretical and methodological dilemmas are often rooted in fundamental philosophical underpinnings, as Turner intimated over a decade
ago in his plenary for the annual Medical Sociology Conference which con-
tained an emphatic plea for the development of sociology of embodiment:

Sociological Cartesianism has blocked the development of
existentialist notions of embodiment. The action categories of
sociology have tended to be hyper-rationalistic, precluding any
fundamental understanding, for example of feelings and emotions.

(Turner 1989: 12)

whereas Freund (1990) maintained that the Durkheimian legacy of
the non-reducibility of 'social facts' to biological 'facts' has resulted in a
lack of acknowledgement of the body in sociology. To understand that
biology can be socially constructed leads to a unification of the cognitive
and the physical aspects of emotions, he claims:

An existential–phenomenological perspective which emphasises
subjectivity and the active expressive body [can be] used to bridge the
mind–body–society splits that characterise both fields . . . a focus on
the emotionally expressive, embodied subject, who is active in the
context of power and social control, can provide a useful approach for
studying distressful feelings, society and health.   (Freund 1990: 452)

---

3. Although established in the United States since the early 1980s, in Britain
this was and is very much a 'new' area treated with some suspicion, possibly
due to the famous British 'reserve', and is only just beginning to be seen on
undergraduate curriculae in the late 1990s.
4. Nettleton and Watson (1998: 4) explain how the term 'the body' becomes
as detached as the Cartesian models themselves and prefer to use the term
'embodiment' which implies a more 'everyday' context.

During the 1990s the body has exploded into the sociological arena with a plethora of texts (see, for example, Featherstone, Hepworth and Turner 1991; Turner 1991, 1992; Shilling 1993; Falk 1994; Martin 1994; Csordas 1994; Butler 1993; Frank 1995, and so on), themed conferences (including the British Sociological Association annual meeting in 1998) and the launch of a new journal, *Body and Society*. In terms of my own orientation to embodiment, particularly influential texts have included feminist phenomenology (see Young 1990; Grosz 1994; Battersby 1998) and Martin's (1987) illuminating cultural analysis of female embodiment, which pulls apart the socially constructed nature of reproductive science. The lynchpin of this study is the *rapprochement* between the natural and the social which links 'lived experience to cultural representation' (Williams and Bendelow 1998a: 165).

Holistic and phenomenological models of embodiment naturally incorporate emotion as a concept; again, social science research has been consistently criticised for its neglect of emotion (Davitz 1969; Hochschild 1983) and many investigations have been concerned with predicting and controlling various emotional phenomena or identifying the antecedents, correlates and consequences of emotional reactions rather than the conceptualisation of these emotional components. Davitz goes as far as to say that:

> Poets and novelists have tried to capture and convey the meaning of emotional experience by a variety of linguistic devices, and of course there have been many instances of successful communication through a literary framework. By and large, psychologists have not been nearly so successful, though occasionally writers like James and Freud break through the bounds of conventional psychology and indeed convey what seem to be rich and valid experiences of emotional experiences. But academically orientated research psychologists have contributed little to this field, and many have taken refuge in the argument that an explication of emotional experience is outside the legitimate realm of scientific psychology. If one wants to learn something about the experience of guilt, anxiety or joy one might turn perhaps to Dostoevsky, Kierkegaard or Wordsworth, but certainly little is to be learned in this area from even the most careful study of Thorndike, Hull, Skinner, or any of the other major figures of academic psychology.
>
> (Davitz 1969: 88)

This neglect is echoed by Hochschild who maintains that social psychologists believe that 'the exquisite care they take to avoid discussing feeling, in order to focus ever more intently and narrowly on cognition, increases the scientific character of the work' (Hochschild 1983: 201). She highlights two strongly held notions which act to confuse and cloud our understanding of emotional processes. First, an emotion such as anger or jealousy is seen to have an independent presence or identity, often given a bodily location or residency in a person or through time (e.g. love in the heart, envy in the bile; we talk of 'expressing' or 'storing' emotions which acquire an identity – 'that old jealousy', etc.). Second, when 'possessed' by emotion we act irrationally and our perceptions are distorted – love is something we fall in or out of, we are in a thrall; we are taken over or consumed by anger, gripped by fear, and so on. The implication is usually negative, and our cultural policy towards our emotional life is to watch out for this and manage it. However, such an attitude negates the positive aspects, such as the instinct to comfort a crying child (Hochschild 1983: 202–3).

Crucially, emotions are socially as well as personally faceted, and their study raises fundamental issues for the mind/body relationship. The attack on biomedicine in the latter half of this century has given more acceptability to the role of emotions in health and illness, the mechanisms by which psychological stress may, at least partly, cause physical illness of various kinds, and the popularity of 'alternative' medicine has encouraged these more holistic models. There has been for some time a considerable literature on the relationship between stress and illness (Pitts and Phillips 1990); there is even the hybrid science of 'psychoneuroimmunology' which shows higher cancer mortality rates for bereaved spouses (Fox 1981; Glaser and Glaser 1986). Similarly, 'life events' research of the type instigated by Brown and Harris (1978; Brown 1996), to look at depression in mothers of dependent children in Camberwell, is given empirical justification with an increasing body of 'findings' supporting psychosomatic links.

As the challenge to the mind/body split gathers momentum, perspectives on emotion are becoming incorporated into accounts of health and illness (James and Gabe 1996) and highly influential in the underpinning of this theoretical framework is the work of Hochschild (1979, 1983, 1998), particularly her concepts of emotional management and emotion work. Drawing on a variety of theorists, including Darwin, Freud, Dewey, Goffman, Gerth and Mills, gives focus in the social context of emotion. Goffman's overarching use of the metaphor of acting, according to which individuals are interpreted as playing characters, plays an important role in informing Hochschild's examination of the control of institutions over our personal feelings. She maintains that 'managing' feelings implies actively altering our emotional state and developing what she terms 'status shields' (1983: 173) in order to protect attacks on our self-esteem. Having one's feelings ignored or termed as irrational has the subsequent impact of one's perceptions being invalidated, of being 'less than a person'. For instance, the feelings of a person of lower status are given less attention and weight than those of higher status, so they have fewer status shields with which to protect themselves. As a consequence, Hochschild maintains that any social theory of emotion must take into account the fact that this process cannot be without cost to the self. It must also recognise the biological basis of emotions, as the means by which we know how we relate to the world, and as therefore crucial to our survival:

> when an emotion signals a message of danger or safety to us, it involves a reality newly grasped on the template of prior expectations. A signal involves a juxtaposition of what we see with what we expect to see – the two sides of surprise. The message 'danger' takes on its meaning of danger only in relation to what we expect.
>
> (Hochschild 1983: 221)

Emotion management may be limited and has its critics – of its ahistoricity Newton (1998) and of its overdeterminism and parallels with rational choice theory (Williams, forthcoming). Nevertheless the concept of 'emotion work' as an emotional estrangement involving the management of bodily states of arousal has obvious implications for the Cartesian dualism of mind and body, and provides an important epistemological starting point for this study. It is also highly salient to the understanding of perceptions of pain.

Gender and pain

Large-scale health surveys carried out in Western industrialised countries have consistently upheld the conundrum that 'women get sick and men die'. In other words, women have a higher life expectancy in terms of mortality, but they also have higher rates of acute and chronic conditions (for a detailed summary of the literature see Annandale 1998). The leading causes of death are degenerative diseases, particularly cardio-vascular and cancer; and males have a higher mortality rate than females in all age groups above five years. However, in underdeveloped countries the picture is more variable; for example in India, Waldron (1983) showed that males have a three-year advantage over females, reflecting factors such as inadequate diet and health care, and especially the associated risks and rigours of pregnancy and childbirth under these conditions. For these reasons, sex differences in life expectancy are sometimes used as an index of economic development. In developed countries, there is increasing evidence that the mortality gap has begun to narrow since 1970, which in turn has implications for the relationship between sex roles and mortality (Verbrugge and Wingard 1987; Annandale 1998).

In addition to the mortality differential, major studies using survey data repeatedly show that, as well as having higher rates of both acute and chronic conditions, women have more restricted activity per condition and record more use of the medical services and higher rates of prescriptions. These higher rates for women obtain even when reproduction and its disorders are excluded. In addition to these physical health differences, there are gender differences in the field of mental health. Women have repeatedly been shown to have higher rates of psychiatric admissions to hospitals, and of GP consultations labelled as psychiatric (Busfield 1988, 1998). Cochrane (1995) has shown that that over-representation occurs selectively, and the female excess is largely due to the categories of depressive psychoses and psychoneuroses and other categories that fall under the broad heading of depression.

The proliferation of interest within social science research in gender differences in morbidity and mortality has resulted in a number of hypotheses being advanced to account for them. These can be grouped into the following categories:

1. *Biological aspects of illness risks*
   Those arising directly from different reproductive functions
   and those linked to aspects of different female/male genetic
   constitutions.

2. *Acquired risks of illness from gender roles*
   Associated stresses of lifestyles, sex-typed occupations, exposure to
   hazards at work or in home, i.e. women have more illness than
   men because their assigned social roles are more stressful.

3. *Different health and illness reporting behaviours*
   Concepts associated with masculinity and femininity such as
   differential childhood socialisation leads males and females to
   differ in their perception, evaluation and response to symptoms.
   Illness reporting behaviour, i.e. women report more illness than
   men do because it is culturally more acceptable for them.

4. *Differential diagnoses and treatments*
   The way in which professional health practitioners view gender
   roles; gender-differentiated access to health services (see Verbrugge
   1990: 41).

Epidemiological patterns of pain appear to repeat the pattern of sex differences in morbidity. For instance, in the United States women report a higher incidence of both temporary and persistent pain than men (see Crooke, Rideout and Browne 1984; von Korff, Dworkin, Le Resche and Kruger 1988), and more women than men seek treatment for chronic pain (Helkimo 1976; Margolis, Zinny, Miller and Taylor 1984). Although contemporary 'scientific' research (Feine, Bushnell, Miron and Duncan 1991) concerned with these differences retains the focus on experimental laboratory testing, there is some acknowledgement that there may be more complex factors involved: 'these differences may be due to sociological factors which demand stoicism in males and allow expression of pain in females, or they may be due to physiologic or anatomical differences between the sexes' (Feine *et al.* 1991: 255). Nevertheless attitude surveys concerned with analgesia conducted by drug companies repeat the view of both sexes that women are much more able to cope with pain than men. For instance, a survey on beliefs about pain (Nurofen 1989) carried out structured interviews of married and heterosexual cohabiting couples over 18 years old, from different areas of the United Kingdom (specified as Scotland, the North, the Midlands, Wales and the South). Of 531 men and women, 229 were classified as social class ABC1 and 302 as C2DE; they were asked to rate their pain threshold and that of their partner on a scale from very low to very high. There were no gender differences whatsoever, but when respondents were asked the question 'Do you believe that women are better able to tolerate pain than men?' 75 per cent of the sample (64 per cent of men and 86 per cent of women) said yes; 15 per cent (20 per cent men and 11 per cent women) thought 'both equally'; the same proportion said they did not know or did not answer; and only 10 per cent (16 per cent men and 3 per cent women) said 'no'. The same question was previously asked in a similar cross-national study in the United States (Squibb 1987). In this study 2,500 married/cohabiting couples were interviewed, and it was found that 82 per cent of the sample felt that the female capacity to cope with pain was much higher.

A more detailed search of the medical and psychiatric literature on pain perception reveals something of a controversy over gender differences. Using a variety of noxious stimuli, such as heat, cold, shock and pressure, some studies confirm the 'no difference' hypothesis (see Lawlis *et al.* 1984; Neri and Agazzani 1984). Other studies, using similar techniques, indicated that women have lower tolerances. For instance, Notermans and Tophoff (1967) found that men were able to tolerate higher intensities of electric shocks than women, but that the detection thresholds did not differ. A study of the reactions of 41,119 men and women by Woodrow *et al.* (1972) showed that men were able to sustain more pressure on the Achilles tendon. Lower pain tolerance or thresholds in females are echoed in other studies (see Otto and Dougher 1985; Dubreuil and Kohn 1986).

Moving away from experimental studies, although there is a wealth of anecdotal evidence about women's pain being somehow not taken as seriously as men's, differential diagnosis is difficult to study and measure, as is any assertion of beliefs and values. Martin (1987) and others have demonstrated how science has devalued the female body since antiquity and historical accounts of medical practice (Ehrenreich and English 1974; Reissman 1989) reveal consistent prejudice towards women by health professionals. Before the time of 'political correctness', this could be overt, as in the following account from the *Maine Medical Journal* entitled 'Painful women' which appeared in 1932:

> Whenever I ask a female to state her symptoms, and she replies, 'I have so many that I have written them on this slip of paper, in order not to forget them', it has a decidedly bearish effect on my spirits. I know, if I let her talk herself out, that eventually she will incriminate herself, albeit in the meantime I am suffering like a she-elephant in the pangs of childbirth, for I am confronted by a hypochondriac. One may indulge in the luxury of terminology here and call these [women] neurasthenics, or psychosthenics, examples of anxiety neurosis or just plain variants. In any case, they are the bane of the average physician's existence, for they tax his medical skill, his tact, his patience and his endurance to a degree not at all commensurate, as a rule, with their ability to pay. The existence of a sociologic problem oftentimes only becomes apparent after painstaking and persistent enquiry. The patient comes with a somatic complaint and carefully conceals her bizarre reaction to an unhappy experience such as a thwarted ambition, a petty jealousy, a husband with the technic of an English sparrow, or a desire to escape the responsibilities of life in the home, or in the business or social world. Examples may also be found among those women who having rushed madly into some much-needed uplift work or reform, only to discover later that their object is unworthy and their noise a lot of ballyhoo, develop symptoms which confine them and thus excuse themselves, because manifestly, one does not expect the sick to work. They include the colourless, uninteresting negative types, who, craving attention (as do all of us more or less) and receiving it not, fly to disease, knowing that illness calls forth sympathy, interest, inquiry, in general, attention, which is the thing desired.   (Gehring 1932: 139–40)

Although the article goes on to make some pertinent connections between emotional states and physiology, the stereotyping of women (and therefore implicitly of men) by male medics is all too obvious and abounds throughout the older literature. Some sixty years later, in an era that is sometimes termed *post-feminist*, it may be argued that we are much enlightened and, indeed, some respondents in the study (male and female) expressed the view that women have achieved equality and thus have no further need to pursue their cause, and that doctors and other health professionals would not differentiate between male or female patients in terms of treatment.

More cynically, a paper by two medical sociologists (a man and a woman) who teach sociological and epidemiological aspects of medicine to medical students at a well-known London teaching hospital (Humphreys and Elford 1990) described how so-called enlightened attitudes may exist only on the surface of public expression. Throughout the term's teaching, students of both sexes consistently displayed public attitudes of awareness of gender and other social issues to both their teachers and their peers. At the end of term, it had become traditional for the students to present an (unevaluated) summary of their learning to their tutors, which could take any form of presentation. The group of students under discussion chose to perform a satirical revue consisting of sketches depicting 'typical' scenarios in a GP surgery. The authors were somewhat dismayed to witness the resulting 'hymn to sexism and cross-dressing, a field-day for parody and stereotype' portrayed with great hilarity by both male and female students. For example, one group examined the relationship between mental health and the social roles of women:

> A distraught woman patient is trying to get into the surgery to see her GP. Meanwhile, the female receptionist is seducing the male doctor. 'Time for your massage, doctor', as she kneads his shoulders. 'Can I take some notes?' as she climbs all over him . . . even when the patient is admitted into the room, the receptionist continues to fawn and frolic. The patient is depressed and talks about her domestic circumstances. Her mother died when she was young, she has three children under the age of five at home, she has no close friends. The 'Professor' then clambers onto the table and starts to lecture us, in an absent-minded way, about vulnerability factors and provoking agents which may explain why the women is depressed, accompanied by much ribald laughter . . .   (Humphreys and Elford 1990: 173)

When the lecturers attempted to set up a meeting to discuss some of the issues raised, in 'a relaxed, non-confrontative manner', they were advised by their senior (medical) colleagues to drop the matter and put it down to 'high jinks' – of course, only *natural* for a group of medical students. This episode was interpreted by the authors as illustrative of the complacency within the medical establishment to perpetrate the status quo of the (heterosexual) male domination of society.

'Political correctness' can, of course, become as closed as the ideologies it criticises and, in talking and theorising about gender, it is important to recognise other forms of social categorisation. Since the 1980s, academic feminism has come under fire from black writers who have criticised the implicit assumption that all women have the same struggles, especially around issues of reproduction and the family. Whereas traditional feminist critiques view the family as the main site of oppression, black feminists such as Bhavnani and Coulson (1986) point out that for many black women the family can be a refuge from the hostile racist world outside. Similarly, black motherhood is often perceived negatively and pathologised (see Anthias and Yuval-Davis 1983; Bryan, Dadzie and Scarfe 1985; Phoenix 1991). Marginalisation also occurs for lesbian and disabled women. In other words, an effective analysis of gender must be cross-cut with other variables such as race and class, as 'women' do not constitute a homogenous group. Age is of great significance also, and although this book does not attempt to look systematically at the elderly or at children as the respondents in study sample were all aged between 18 and 65, these groups are likewise subjected to subjugation, and *in extremis* seen almost as a lesser species (Mayall 1996; Hockey and James 1993; James, Jenks and Prout 1998).

Within the context of the present study, however, the focus on gender is particularly appropriate with regard to the development of a phenomeno-logical sociological approach to pain. Feminist theory has had an important impact on the development of qualitative methodology. Although theoret-ical approaches to pain have broadened out since the 1960s, becoming more eclectic and multi-disciplinary, and encompassing both phenomenological and hermeneutic philosophies, these developments do not, so far, appear to be reflected in the methodological design of studies.

Thus gender is used almost as a case study, a lens through which to view the prism of pain, as one of its many aspects. It is also particularly apposite given the methodological contribution that has been made by feminist scholars, much of whose work has been grounded in ethnographic and humanistic traditions and philosophies, the essential feature being to emphasise the subjective (see, for example, Oakley 1981; Finch 1984; Smith 1988; Harding 1987; Ribbens and Edwards 1997). Indeed, Oakley (1998) goes as far to say that it is methodology itself that is fundament-ally gendered.

An explicit agenda involved in employing a phenomenological methodology is that it aims to reveal the 'lay' voice rather than that of the 'expert' or professional. In turn, this enables the discussion of feelings and emotions to take place. The central aim of this research is to explore how men and women perceive, evaluate and act upon their own symptoms of pain, and whether social characteristics, particularly gender, are seen to be important in affecting this process. Existing research suggests that the understanding and interpretation of personal beliefs about affliction and pain are a fundamental component of pain perception. These beliefs include emotional, psychological, sociological, philosophical and existential aspects, as well as the sensory dimensions. A central hypothesis of the present research is that the dominance of a somatic ideology inherent in medicine tends to define emotional expression in experiences of pain as socially undesirable, whereas its suppression through mechanisms such as stoicism tend to be highly valued. It is further hypothesised that this moral evaluation may be gendered.

chapter 3

Researching pain: responses from the GP waiting room

The aim of this research was to initiate an exploratory phenomenological approach to the perception of pain, with a focus on the role of gender in the formation of pain beliefs. The theoretical background is diverse and draws upon sociology of health and illness; emotions and embodiment; chronic illness and illness narratives; gender differences in mortality, morbidity and health service use; and feminist methodology. A substantial number of unsolved questions are raised in these areas both in relation to the ways in which experiences relating to pain are gender differentiated and to the explanations for any such differences. As the sociological literature on pain is relatively sparse, a variety of psychological, medical, philosophical and anthropological sources have also been considered.

The fieldwork for the research was undertaken in two stages. The sample was obtained via a GP surgery in an inner-city area of North London which has a very mixed social profile. Data collection took place over a period of nine months in 1989 and 1990. Using the principles of triangulation, a questionnaire was designed to attempt to examine the beliefs about health, illness and pain of a wider population; to collect social, demographic and medical information; and to engender themes that would be examined in more depth by an interview sub-sample. The questionnaire was administered in a GP surgery and was completed by 107 men and women. In the second stage of fieldwork a more qualitative approach was adopted and a sub-sample of 21 people took part in the in-depth interviews, which explored the complexities of attitudes and beliefs about the nature of pain, both from personal experience and through responses to the predicaments of others presented by a series of visual images. Key questions in both instruments addressed general health beliefs, experiences of illness and pain, the role of emotions in pain perception, the perceived ability of men and women to cope with pain, and the importance (or not) of other variables such as race and class in shaping pain experiences. The research questions were not confined to chronic pain, encompassing any experience the subjects themselves defined as pain, either in the past or in the present.

The research presented in the study falls into the category defined by Brannen as 'the pre-eminence of the qualitative over the quantitative' (1989: 36). In this, quantitative methods are subservient to the qualitative ones. They provide background data in which to contextualise a small-scale and intensive piece of work. The questionnaire used in the study provided a wider sample, whose characteristics could be compared to those deployed in other health surveys. The opinions and beliefs about pain revealed in the questionnaire study formed the basis of the in-depth work. A major objective was to explore respondents' own feelings about their experiences of pain, in order to produce interpretative rather than clinical data. In contrast to more traditional methods of 'measuring' pain, the analysis of the interview data shows that the meanings and definitions of pain to the individual are not confined to physical sensations, but incorporate feelings and emotions, even spiritual and existential notions. And, as noted earlier, the complexity of these beliefs proved much more difficult to access by questionnaire format.

In a critique of the implicit gender bias within the methodology of social research, Graham (1983: 132) points out that the survey method reflects the dominant social values of the time it was conceived, namely the principles of individualism, equivalence and rationality. Although those values may accord with those that govern the operation of the state and the economy, it is more difficult to apply them to women's work in and for the family. Graham argues that although the use of this model distorts the lived reality of the everyday world, particularly the unequal social network of relationships which characterises women's lives, to reject it completely would be detrimental:

> Surveys, precisely because they conform to the rules of the public domain, have played an important part in raising the consciousness of those within the scientific and political world. Much of our knowledge about the position and problems of women, knowledge crucial to the promotion (and preservation) of less divisive policies in the field of employment, health and education, derives from survey research. However, this method cannot be employed uncritically.
>
> (Graham 1983: 135)

This returns us to the need for a *rapprochement* between different methodological approaches which emerged from the areas of work discussed previously. Methodological issues are raised by the above considerations, as traditional clinical or experimental studies are unable to encompass the more abstract and subjective aspects of pain beliefs. There may be variation in acute or chronic, physical or emotional components, depending on the individual's experience. Hence, a principal aim of this study is to allow the subjects to define for themselves what they mean by 'pain'. The inclusion of subjective approaches in the research design makes even more apposite the focus on gender, as theoretical and methodological work within the sociology of health and illness by feminist scholars over the last fifteen years has highlighted the links between qualitative methodology and the representation of gendered experiences. (It is recognised, however, that gender does not operate in isolation, being cross-cut by other social characteristics such as race and class.) In addition, much of this work is grounded in ethnographic and humanistic traditions, an essential feature of which is to emphasise the subjective and to reveal the 'lay' voice rather than that of the 'expert' or professional.

Feminist critiques within medical sociology have identified a long-standing and unquestioning acceptance of the values and norms of the existing society which are reflected in medical practice and provision (see Clarke 1983). As a discipline, sociology has the flexibility and 'methodological imagination' required to allow insights into the complexity of pain beliefs, as located in the context of such issues. Sociologists have consistently argued that the blending of quantitative and qualitative approaches can be complementary, and that the logic of triangulation lends itself to one set of data being 'checked' against another (Bryman 1988). This is the approach used in the design of the present study. Central to the research design are three different but complementary methods of data collection:

1.   A questionnaire survey.
2.   An in-depth interview.
3.   A vignette technique involving a discussion of visual imagery portraying various types of pain experience.

The remainder of this chapter focuses on the findings from the questionnaire responses, whereas the findings from the other data sets are discussed in the following three chapters, with a summary of the findings in Chapter 6.

The questionnaire survey

The questionnaire phase of the study had two main objectives. The first was to examine beliefs about health, illness and pain within a larger population than could be included in an interview sample (bearing in mind the time and cost constraints of a doctoral study). A second objective was to suggest themes that could be examined by means of in-depth interviews with a smaller sample.

Kilburn is a multi-racial inner-city area with a very mixed social profile, including both deprivation and gentrification in housing and other services. There is a large Irish population, many of whom are third generation, and also a sizeable part of the community is second or third generation to parents who originally emigrated from the Caribbean. Many of the respondents who described themselves as 'mixed race' have parents from either or both of these two cultures.

The questionnaire sample was obtained by writing to a number of GP surgeries and health centres in North and Central London between October 1988 and March 1989 and explaining the aims of the research. I was kindly allowed access to a patient sample from a GP practice in Kilburn, North West London, on the understanding that patient records, names and addresses would only be obtained with the patient's consent. Young people under the age of 18 were excluded, in order to avoid complications with parental consent. The random sample was to be based on the practice population of 10,189 men and women aged 17+, but which had a lower than average proportion of men and women aged over 65 (only 7 per cent in this age range).

It was decided to aim for 100 cases in order to provide a realistically manageable sample which would yield meaningful statistics. A postal survey was planned following the recommendations of Cartwright (1984) and Oakley (1992), who have achieved high response rates with postal health surveys. Cautiously aiming for a response rate of 50 per cent, 200 questionnaires were sent out by calculating the proportions in each group and randomly selecting names and addresses according to the age/ sex register. The questionnaires were sent out by the practice manager, as this was considered 'ethically' preferable to allowing me direct access to names and addresses. Unfortunately, these efforts met with little success. Out of the 200 questionnaires that were sent out in June 1989 with introductory letters from the surgery, only 19 replies had been received by the end of July. A reminder with a duplicate questionnaire sent in August only yielded another 13 responses, giving a total of 32 (of which only four had been filled in by men).

Although postal questionnaires have produced good response rates in other health surveys, Cartwright (1984) observes that interest in and commitment to the subject is needed. It may have been the case that the questionnaire presented pain in too broad a manner, or that it is too sensitive as a topic. Other factors could have contributed to the poor response rate, including the tendency of response rates to be consistently lower in the London area. However, a significant factor was that sixty-five questionnaires – 33 per cent of the initial mailing – were returned marked 'not known at this address'. When this was reported back to the practice manager, the records were cross-checked from the computer and only three changes of address had been notified. The lack of reliability of records in inner-city practices has been noted by others (Jarman 1983). As well as raising policy issues, this was a valuable lesson in terms of using GP records for research purposes, as previous concerns expressed by members of the practice had centred on the ethical issues rather than any practical difficulties.

Following the low response rate to the postal questionnaire, it was decided that the most sensible strategy would be to abandon the postal survey and devise another way of distributing the questionnaires. Permission was obtained for me to approach patients in the surgery waiting room to take part in the research, again on the understanding that contact remained totally confidential and anonymous unless the person concerned volunteered their name and/or address. From September until mid-November 1989 I attended the surgery whenever possible, ensuring that different days of the week and different times of the day were covered (for example, morning and evening surgeries). I was allowed to sit at the reception desk and to approach anyone who registered for an appointment to see if they would be willing to complete the questionnaire. In this way I was able to collect a total of seventy-five cases. Only five people among those I approached refused to participate. The cases were sampled to be as representative as possible of the practice profile. In eleven of these cases, I read the questionnaire aloud to the person concerned and filled it in for them, as they either had visual impairment or other difficulties with reading, or else English was not their primary language and some explanation of the questions was needed. The other respondents completed the questionnaires themselves, usually within the time they waited to see the doctor (I made it clear that I was available if there were any queries). The final version of the questionnaire comprised mainly pre-coded questions and covered the following broad topics:

1.   Medical history and general health beliefs.

2.   Worst experience of pain (using pain scales to evaluate past experience).

3.   'Coping' behaviour in illness and pain, i.e. action taken, whether treatment was sought, satisfaction with outcome.

4.   The importance of the role of emotions in perceptions of pain.

5.   Expectations relating to the ability of men and women to cope with painful experiences – whether there are differences and why.

6.   Open space was given for respondents to include anything that they thought was relevant to their experiences of or beliefs about pain.

As a central hypothesis of the thesis was that social factors may give rise to variations in pain perception, demographic details in addition to gender and age were collected, including occupational status, household type and tenure, ethnic background, age of leaving school and qualifications gained. Once the questionnaires were completed, coding frames were developed for the majority of the open-ended questions and the data were analysed by SPSS PC using the chi-square test (some of the responses to open questions did not lend themselves to this form of analysis, either because the responses were too complex to reduce into a coding frame, or there were too few to be able to do so).

Survey sample

The profile of the questionnaire sample with detail on age and sex is shown in Table 1. Data on social class, educational background, housing tenure and ethnicity were also collected. Using the Registrar-General's classification of occupation, the social class distribution overall was 41 per cent in so-called 'middle-class' occupations and 59 per cent 'working-class', with more women than men in social classes II and III non-manual and more men in III manual, IV and V.[1] There were no significant class differences in ethnic background although those of Irish descent were more likely

---

1.   Although sociodemographic data collected in this way, in particular using the Registrar-General's classification, are notoriously unreliable, especially as regards gender, I felt it was justified in terms of being used descriptively rather than for statistical inferences.

Table 1: Age/sex profile of Kilburn sample.

	Females		Males		Total	
	%	(N)	%	(N)	%	(N)
18–24	19	(10)	15	(8)	17	(18)
25–44	48	(26)	48	(25)	48	(51)
45–64	22	(12)	25	(13)	24	(25)
Over 65	11	(6)	12	(6)	11	(12)
TOTAL	100	(54)	100	(52)	100	(106)

Note: 1 missing case.

to be in the manual category. Information on education was collected by asking at what age the respondents left school and whether they had any formal qualifications. Fifty-two per cent of the sample (57 per cent of women, 47 per cent of men) had left school at age 16 or under, compared to 48 per cent (43 per cent of women and 53 per cent of men) who had stayed on. 'School' had different connotations to some of those educated outside the UK system, as some respondents indicated that they had not left until the age of 21. Higher school-leaving age and formal qualifications correlated significantly with higher occupational status. In this sample, although women are more likely to have school-leaving qualifications, men are more likely to have achieved higher degrees. As regards housing tenure, only a third of the sample were owner-occupiers, with others living in privately rented or social housing, reflecting the high mobility and housing turnover in the area. Twenty per cent of the sample lived alone, a third with a partner, and a quarter with a partner and one or more children. As to ethnicity, 6 per cent were Asian, 21 per cent Black British, 20 per cent Irish, and 46 per cent White British (the categories are refined from an open-ended question asking respondents to define for themselves their nationality and ethnic origins).[2] The sample is representative of the adult population of this particular practice, but may show some local idiosyncrasies compared to larger surveys such as the *General Household Survey* (OPCS 1994).

---

2. 'Asian' may be British and includes ethnic origins from India, Pakistan, China. 'Black British' includes African/Caribbean and Caribbean/Irish. 'Irish' includes second- and third-generation persons from the Republic defining themselves as such. 'White British' includes Scottish, Welsh, English and Northern Irish. 'Other' includes North American, Italian, Cypriot, other European and Libyan.

Table 2:   Self-reported health status of Kilburn sample.

	Females		Males		All	
	%	(N)	%	(N)	%	(N)
OVERALL HEALTH						
Excellent	14	(7)	21	(11)	17	(18)
Reasonable	86	(46)	75	(39)	81	(85)
Poor	0	(0)	4	(2)	2	(2)
TOTAL	100	(53)	100	(52)	100	(105)
Significance = P > 0.1						
OVER LAST 12 MONTHS						
Excellent	9	(5)	20	(10)	14	(15)
Reasonable	89	(48)	73	(38)	81	(86)
Poor	2	(1)	7	(4)	5	(5)
TOTAL	100	(54)	100	(52)	100	(106)
No significance						

Experiences of illness and pain: survey findings

Presentation of the survey findings below falls into two sections: self-reported health and general health beliefs; and experiences of pain, and beliefs about gender and pain. To clarify comparisons between the findings of this research and other surveys such as the *General Household Survey* (GHS), the sample in this study will be referred to as the 'Kilburn sample'.

Self-reported health and general health beliefs

Health status

Respondents were asked to rate their own health, both overall and over the last year: the answers are shown by gender in Table 2, and men are significantly more likely than women to rate their health as excellent or as poor. The higher social classes are more likely to rate their health as excellent, and an increase in age correlates with an increase in poorer health rating. There are no obvious ethnic differences. These results can be compared to a similar survey of self-reported health measures of a random sample of 211 patients over 18 drawn from the records of a group practice (Blaxter 1985). Taking into account that the ratings of the two studies are different, in that the 'excellent' and 'poor' of the Kilburn study are more extreme than the categories used in Blaxter's study ('above average',

'average' and 'below average'), the same pattern of men being more likely to report good health emerges. Forty-five per cent of men reported above average health, compared to 36 per cent of women, whereas more women (22 per cent) reported 'below average' health than men (11 per cent) in this sample.

Non-manual men report their health as above average, whereas both men and women in manual categories are more likely to rate their health status as below average. These social class differences fit with evidence about the relationship between lower socioeconomic class and ill health described earlier.

Long-term illness, disability or impediment

Respondents were asked whether they suffered from any long-standing illness, disability or infirmity, with the following qualifying explanation: 'for example, anything physical such as diabetes, arthritis, back pain; anything involving loss of functioning such as deafness, lameness, etc. or anything emotional such as depression, anxiety etc.'. They were also asked how long they had had the condition and how severely it affected their lives, whether they received any treatment and how satisfactory the treatment was. Half of the males in the sample reported that they suffered from a condition of this nature, compared to 33 per cent of females. Responses to the question about whether their condition affected their daily life compared with similar findings from the GHS.[3]

In contrast with the national picture, the males in the Kilburn sample have an excess of morbidity over females. Three features of the sample are relevant here: first, the problem of smaller numbers; second, the fact that there were more men in the manual social class categories than women, thus increasing morbidity rates; and third, the questionnaire was administered in the GP surgery waiting room, implying that respondents would be likely to be visiting their GP for treatment of a particular complaint. The most common complaint was chronic back pain; other categories were very diverse with few numbers in each and covered arthritis, diabetes, hypertension, loss of sight/hearing, psychiatric conditions and post-operative complications.

Last short-term illness

The questionnaire was administered in the waiting room of the surgery so the responses covered a very wide range of complaints, which are

---

3. The GHS is an annual survey based on a sample of the general population resident in private households in Great Britain.

condensed into twelve categories in descending order of reporting. These are as follows: influenza, upper respiratory infection, gastro-intestinal disorders, circulatory problems, skin conditions, gynaecological problems, asthma, migraine, accidents, psychiatric conditions, other infections, other conditions.

Health beliefs

Using the model of Blaxter's health and lifestyle study (1985), open-ended questions asked whether respondents thought there were aspects of their lifestyles that affected their health. Some examples were listed, and most of the respondents simply ticked or underlined factors that they thought appropriate such as smoking/not smoking; abuse of alcohol/not drinking; illegal drugs; bad diet/proper diet; (lack of) exercise, fresh air; overeating, obesity/moderation in eating; anything in excess/moderation in all things; (lack of) sleep/rest. The most positive influences on health were thought to be exercise and fresh air (45 per cent) and a proper diet (38 per cent). Other factors were given less than 10 per cent ratings as positive attributes. Of the written responses, very few differed from the examples given, but some included broad topics such as religion, love, friends and happiness in the positive factors. The factor thought to have the most negative effect on health was overwhelmingly that of smoking (61 per cent) and respondents in this sample gave high ratings to overwork, boredom and stress. Other factors mentioned in the pre-coded list used for the Kilburn sample did not receive substantial ratings (e.g. alcohol 8 per cent; poor diet 6 per cent; pain 3 per cent). The 'added-in' negative aspects were even fewer, but were more specific, such as genetic factors or emotional difficulties (for example, effects of bereavement, divorce, etc.) which were not subsumed in the general 'stress' category.

Pain

Worst experience of pain

One open-ended question asked: 'Could you describe the worst pain you've ever had, and what you think caused it?' The question was asked in this way in order to explore what individuals would define as pain. The responses are classified in Table 3. Gender differences are obvious in the experience of childbirth, but also in the larger numbers of men in the accident/injury category. The range of experiences was very extensive, and difficult to reduce into categories. For example, the accident/injury category included broken bones, burns, sprains, being shot in the ear with

Table 3:   Most painful experience in Kilburn sample.

	Females		Males		All	
	%	(N)	%	(N)	%	(N)
Accident/injury	19	(10)	29	(15)	24	(25)
Infection/illness	19	(10)	17	(9)	18	(19)
Back pain	9	(5)	17	(9)	14	(14)
Childbirth	17	(9)	—	—	9	(9)
Migraine	8	(4)	6	(3)	7	(7)
Surgical	8	(4)	5	(3)	6	(7)
Emotional/psych.	5	(3)	2	(1)	4	(4)
Other	6	(4)	15	(8)	11	(12)
None/not answered	9	(5)	9	(5)	7	(10)
TOTAL	100	(54)	100	(53)	100	(107)

an air rifle, being run over by a car, being knocked off a bicycle, being beaten as a child, being mugged and having a piece of grit embedded in the eye. Infections and illnesses included appendicitis, tonsillitis, pleurisy, gallstones, perforated ulcers, kidney infections, middle ear infections, colitis, mouth abscesses and an infected blister on the hand. The pains described as surgical were post-operative wounds, a skin graft and amputation of an arm and leg. 'Other' included toothache, trapped nerves, indigestion, cramp, menstrual pain and 'cold turkey' (withdrawal from heroin addiction). Only 4 per cent (three women and one man) of the sample gave responses that did not involve obvious physical trauma, namely the death of a mother, the break-up of a marriage, having to leave the parental home, and being informed of HIV-positive status.

Pain scales

Pain scales have been consistently used to measure subjective responses (see Melzack 1975). In order to provide some comparative data, respondents were asked to rate how painful they thought an injection or blood test was on a scale of 1–6, and then to do the same with their most painful experience. Although ratings for the worst pain ever experienced revealed few differences in the ratings of those who filled them in, women gave somewhat higher pain ratings to the blood test/injection score. This finding is consistent with the hypothesis that women are more likely to report less severe symptoms of morbidity (Verbrugge 1985). Alternatively, the pain associated with blood tests may be more salient for women because, as Popay and Bartley (1989) point out, women are more likely to have experienced this type of health check more recently and more frequently, and men are more likely to 'divorce' themselves from the experience. Women who had experienced childbirth were also asked to rate that experience on the same scale. Of the eighteen women who completed this question, ten scored extreme pain (6), six scored moderate (3–4) and two scored mild pain (1–2).

The role of emotions in perceptions of pain

Table 4 shows that men were substantially less inclined than women to place importance on the emotional component of pain perception, certainly in terms of fear, anxiety and depression.

This was a very difficult topic to raise in questionnaire format, reflected in the large numbers of missing cases. In the categories of anxiety and fear, twice as many men as women did not respond, despite completing the rest of the questionnaire.

Coping with pain: social expectations of men and women

With regard to coping, questions were asked about both behaviour and attitudes. There were no discernible gender differences in coping behaviour:

Table 4: Perceived effects of emotion on pain in Kilburn sample.

	Females		Males		Total		
	%	(N)	%	(N)	%	(N)	
Anxiety							
Little or no effect	37	(17)	60	(22)	47	(39)	
Considerable effect	63	(30)	40	(15)	53	(45)	
TOTAL	100	(47)	100	(37)	100	(84)	
Missing		(7)		(16)		(23)	Significance = P < 0.01
Depression							
Little or no effect	37	(15)	58	(21)	47	(36)	
Considerable effect	63	(27)	42	(15)	53	(42)	
TOTAL	100	(42)	100	(36)	100	(78)	
Missing		(12)		(17)		(29)	Significance = P < 0.01
Fear							
Little or no effect	34	(14)	46	(14)	39	(28)	
Considerable effect	66	(29)	54	(16)	61	(45)	
TOTAL	100	(43)	100	(30)	100	(73)	
Missing		(11)		(23)		(34)	Significance = P < 0.1

30 per cent of men and 36 per cent of women sought treatment for their last short-term illness, either by self-medication or seeing their GP. Twelve women and fifteen men (28 per cent of the sample) reported being in pain at the time of the questionnaire. Of these twenty-seven people, twenty-three sought treatment from their GP, two from an osteopath, one from a physiotherapist and one obtained medication from the chemist.

The question asked in the survey about gender-differentiated perceptions of coping with pain attempted to be more neutral than the market research described in the last chapter (Nurofen 1989). It asked whether respondents thought that there were any differences in the capacities of men and women to cope with pain. Although the findings were not as extreme as the Nurofen market research, the men in the Kilburn sample were still more likely to say that there were no differences between men and women, with only a minority of both sexes weighted towards men coping better.

The survey data also included some open-ended material on the reasons given for these opinions, filled in by some respondents. As these data relate to explanations of one of the significant gender differences found in the survey as a whole, it seemed appropriate to apply the analytical framework described in detail in Chapter 2, which uses four explanations of gender differences in morbidity. Many responses could be categorised into the nature/culture dichotomy, utilising either explanatory themes that were biological or theories of socialisation or social roles (see Figure 5).

Figure 5:   Nature *versus* culture: biological, role and socialisation explanations of pain-coping behaviour.

RESPONSES USING BIOLOGICAL EXPLANATIONS OF MEN'S AND WOMEN'S PAIN-COPING BEHAVIOUR

'Women cope better': 50% of total sample

Females   It's a sexual difference, women are built that way.
            Women go through things like childbirth.
Males   Childbirth.
            Because I have seen the pain my wife has been through in childbirth.
            Men and women are made of the same 'stuff' – other than
                reproduction.
            It's physiological.

'Men cope better': 12% of total sample

Females   Men are stronger.
            Because of physical ability.
Males   Men are stronger.
            Physical differences.

Figure 5: (contd)

'No differences': 33% of total sample

Females We all have the same central nervous system.
Males They are both human.
Because pain is pain.
After all we are the same.

RESPONSES USING ROLES AND 'SOCIALISATION' EXPLANATIONS OF MEN'S AND WOMEN'S PAIN-COPING BEHAVIOUR

'Women cope better': 50% of total sample

Females Full-time routine to carry out.
Women usually just have to get on with it because of kids and jobs.
It's more a state of mind.
It depends on an individual's character or attitudes, not whether they are male or female.
Men are more childish.
Because of societal conditioning and necessity.
Women are conditioned to cope with more pain.
Men can be big babies.
Men show more feelings of pain, women control them.
Men just don't like pain.
Women have to cope, no choice.
Men are just like little boys.
Men are just babies.
Males The average man always thinks he's tougher than he is but is not so good at coping with pain when it happens.

'Men cope better': 12% of total sample

Females Men do not show pain as much and therefore are able to cope with it whereas women express pain more.
Males Men are more relaxed, less anxious.
Men have more determination, so can put things off.

'No differences': 33% of total sample

Females There's a popular myth of men as bad patients – it's not true except that it may affect behaviour and expectations of behaviour but it seems unlikely to be sex-defined.
It depends upon the person, it's not sex-determined.
It depends on the individual and how much patience they have.
Males People harden themselves against pain. Throughout our lives we undergo painful events.
It's more a state of mind.
It depends on an individual's character or attitudes, not whether they are male or female.

Figure 6: Nature *and* culture: holistic explanations of men's and women's pain-coping behaviour.

'Women cope better': 50% of total sample

Females Women get more used to pain because of dysmenorrhoea, etc.
Women are stronger emotionally, due to the menstrual cycle
and child labour they are more prepared for pain and their
tolerance is highest.
Mentally women are stronger and have to cope with regular
physical pain and are therefore more used to it.
I just think women can endure a lot more than men generally,
both emotionally and physically.
Women are made to suffer pain through periods and childbirth.
Whatever social climate, women end up child-rearing, therefore
they don't have the privilege of giving in to pain and sickness.
Nature has built women that way to cope with everyday
pressures – raising a family, running a home, etc.
Because there are more illnesses and problems that women have
to face – all throughout her life a woman is different.
Women give birth. Most women just have to get on with it
whereas men can be mothered.
Men give in to pain easier, but women (especially mothers)
soldier on, they have no choice as children need caring for.
Women usually have to care for others and are not able to take
to their beds as easily as men.

Males Women have more physical awareness – a more intimate and
responsible instinct to their biology; all we do is shave.
Pain affects different people in different ways. Men feel they have
to cover up pain as it is supposedly a sign of weakness.
Women have more strength, they don't moan so much.
Often women experience frequent pain and learn to deal with it.
It's well-known fact that men – and I'm one – can't stand pain.
Women take things in their stride.

'No differences': 12% of total sample

Females It depends on the pain threshold of the individual.
It's more a question of how they express it, how they deal with it,
there's a difference in the social acceptability of expressing pain.

Males I feel that there are determining factors other than what sex the
person is.

Table 5:   Characteristics of interview sample.

Women	F1	F2	F3	F4	F5
Age	33	29	67	38	37
Occupation	Musician p.t.	Childcare f.t.	Ex-nurse retired	Secretary f.t.	Childcare f.t.
Ethnicity Nationality	White British	Nigerian English British	White British	White British	White British
Tenure	Owner occupier	Council	Owner occupier	Council	Owner occupier
Most pain	Brain tumour operation	3rd labour	Fractured skull	Peritonitis	Tooth abscess

Men	M1	M2	M3	M4	M5
Age	28	23	38	25	66
Occupation	Double glazing salesman f.t.	Freelance copywriter p.t.	Artist/ decorator p.t.	Actor p.t. Out of work	Dentist (retired)
Ethnicity Nationality	White Irish	Jewish/ German	White British	White British	White British
Tenure	Parental home	Parental home	Owner occupier	Squat	Owner occupier
Most pain	Beaten by father as a child	Migraine	Infection of leg vein	Toothache/panic attacks	Injection for tennis elbow

However, as Figure 6 shows, these categories proved too simplistic for some replies which encompassed more than one of these explanations and were more likely to be given by women than men. The more sophisticated explanations embrace *all* of the hypotheses advanced to explain gender differences in morbidity, are able to transcend nature and culture and are less 'essentialist'.

In summary, the data from the questionnaire survey presented in this chapter can be shown to reveal the following differences between men and women in perceptions and beliefs regarding pain. First, men were significantly less inclined than women to think that the emotional component of pain perception had any importance. Second, more people perceived women to have a superior capacity to men for coping with pain or, if not, that there were no gender differences; a minority said that men were better at coping with pain. When asked to expand upon why

F6	F7	F8	F9	F10	F11
18	47	36	56	34	28
School	Charity fundraiser f.t.	Social worker f.t.	Cleaner p.t.	Health worker f.t.	Shop assistant f.t.
Polish/Jewish British	White British	African/Irish British	White Irish	White British	White Irish
Parental home	Owner occupier	Private furnished	Council	Private furnished	Housing co-op.
Scalding	Back injury	Death of mother	Nursing husband with Alzheimer's disease	Skin graft for leg operation	Back pain

M6	M7	M8	M9	M10	M11
50	35	36	40	62	27
Housing admin. worker f.t.	Kitchen porter p.t.	Musician f.t.	Never worked due to heroin addiction	Ex-journalist (invalidity benefit)	Scrap-yard dealer f.t.
White British	White British	White British	White British	White S. African	White Irish
Housing co-op.	Council	Housing co-op.	Council	Council	Council
Toothache	Forcible ECT	Infected blister on hand	Kidney transplant	Leg amputation	Learning of HIV positive status

respondents made their choices, the reasons given involved theories of socialisation and roles as well as biological explanations.

The fact that the longer the written responses to this open-ended question were, the more complex was the explanation, suggested that alternative research methods might enable this quite intricate set of beliefs to be explored in more depth. The next stage of the research design attempted to explore these phenomena in the context of respondents' own homes or environments of their own choice, rather than a GP surgery, and using much more in-depth methods.

At the end of the questionnaire, respondents were asked to leave a name and address or telephone number if they were willing to take part in any further research. Thirty-one respondents (sixteen women and fifteen men) volunteered initially, but when I made contact with them, four people had moved from the address given and five were not willing to participate any more, despite agreeing initially. In two cases, I was unable to elicit the reasons for the reluctance to participate as the respondents either failed to turn up at the arranged meeting place or to answer the door. In each case, I made three attempts to arrange to meet without success. The reasons given by the other three were as follows: one man told me over the telephone that, being a black person, he was unhappy about talking to a white researcher; another refused to participate as he had assumed that it would be a television interview; and one woman arranged a meeting at her workplace but later apologetically cancelled, as she said that her husband did not wish her to take part. So eventually, eleven men and eleven women took part in the interview (see Table 5 for sample characteristics). The interview was arranged, usually in the respondent's home, although three people used their workplace and two came to the research unit as they did not wish me to visit their home.

Throughout this volume, pseudonyms are used in order to protect the respondents' confidentiality.

chapter 4

'She's a picture of universal anguish': visual images of pain

The aim of the second stage of the fieldwork was to examine the themes of the questionnaire in greater depth, and to provide deeper insights into the complexity of pain beliefs and perceptions by using a more subjective approach which would enable definitions of pain to be both broadened out and more contextualised. Just as psychologists have despaired as to whether the language of social science could be used to convey emotion, attempts by medics to provide a taxonomy of pain reveal similar limitations in the powers of expression, as this physician laments:

> To demonstrate their distress, most people readily offer dramatic
> affective language, describing pain in terms of tension, fear and
> autonomic distress. Expressions such as exhausting, frightful and
> sickening are often accompanied by paralinguistic vocalisations of
> moaning and groaning and non-verbal signs of affective discomfort to
> signal the sufferer's distress to observers.   (Craig 1984: 153)

In other words, any study of perceptions of and beliefs about pain has to grapple with the tensions of the striving of technical scientific language towards neutral objectivity which is discordant with the human ability to convey emotional and experiential qualities of pain. However, this is not to suggest that subjective, qualitative approaches have *never* been utilised in pain research, and indeed within medicine and clinical diagnosis.

Subjective measures of pain

'Pain narratives' is a short historical account by Bayliss (in Greenhalgh and Hurwitz 1998) of the work of Sir John Ryle, a consultant physician at Guy's Hospital, London, in pre-NHS days. *Ryle's checklist* which, according to Bayliss, was used prolifically until technology such as ECG machines took over, relied entirely on interpreting patient accounts of their pain for diagnosis, using the following criteria:

- Situation

- Radiation

- Localisation

- Character

- Severity

- Duration

- Frequency

- Relieving

- Aggravating

- Special times

- Associated symptoms   (Ryle 1949 quoted in Bayliss 1998: 78)

Subjective measures emphasise the importance of language and expression and have been extensively developed in palliative care and to some degree in pain clinics over the last thirty years, initiated largely by Ronald Melzack (1975: 277–99). The adjectives are divided into three groups: sensory, affective and evaluative. The McGill Pain Questionnaire requires respondents to choose the order of the words on a rating scale to imply their intensity and the nature of their pain.

Within psychomedical research, subjective measures of pain have even utilised imagery as a research tool. For instance, the Pain Apperception Test (PAT) was developed by Petrovich (1957) to measure pain reactivity. He tried to show that each individual is predisposed to perceive pain experienced by others in a characteristic and relatively constant manner, stemming from the individual's own experience of and reactions to pain. The test consists of twenty-five cards depicting a male in his middle thirties in various painful situations, divided into three main groups: the first group depicts felt sensations with examples such as a man seated on a bed and clutching his stomach with his right hand, a man who has shot himself in the shoulder with a rifle, a kneeling man who has been shocked while working on an electrical outlet, and a swimmer who injures his toe on a beach chair beside the pool. The second group depicts anticipation vs. felt sensation with such examples as a man about to receive a hypodermic injection in the deltoid, followed by the same scenario but with the hypodermic actually inserted, and a man being seated in a dentist's chair about to have his tooth drilled, followed by the dental drill inside his mouth. The final group is designated self-inflicted vs. other-inflicted, as in the following scenarios: a man hits his thumb with a hammer while driving a nail, and the second picture has a second person wielding the hammer; a man removes foreign matter from his eye with a handkerchief and in the second picture another person is holding the handkerchief; and so on (Petrovich 1957: 343–4).

The respondents, 100 (presumably male) patients of the Veterans Administration Hospital at St Louis, Missouri, were asked to score the projected intensity and duration of pain on a seven-point scale for each situation by answering the following:

1. How does the man feel? (Answers: no pain, hardly any pain, some pain, moderate amount of pain, much pain, very much pain, can't stand the pain.)

2. How long will it hurt him? (Answers: not at all, seconds, minutes, hours, days, weeks, months.)

The study was unusual in that the focus was on reaction rather than sensation, attempting to tap the emotional response to painful situations experienced by others. Petrovich claimed that high scores on the PAT correlated significantly with anxiety and neuroticism, using Taylor's Manifest Anxiety Scale (1953) and Eysenck's Personality Inventory (1956). Despite the imaginative methodological approach which allowed access to emotional responses, the study was heavily criticised by the scientific community on the grounds that it proved difficult to replicate. Identification with the sufferer in the test cards was thought to differ from subject to subject (the point that this may have been a gender issue, as the subject was male, was not raised).

These criticisms appear to have effectively curtailed any further development of the technique until Elton, Quarry, Burrows and Stanley (1978) tried to replicate it in Melbourne twenty years later. They argued that the imagery material was considered too complex and ambiguous by the subjects and that the extraneous clues were too confusing. Subsequently, they developed a new measure which they named the Melbourne Pain Apperception Film (MPAF) which depicted a bare hand and forearm in situations of increasing pain as follows:

1. Hand slapped.

2. Hand pinched.

3. Finger pricked with a pin.

4. Hand hit with a wooden ruler.

5. Thumb hit by a hammer.

6. Hand caught in a door.

7. Fingers burnt by a match.

8. Hot water spilled on a hand.

9. Hand cut deeply on the ball of thumb by a knife.

10. Fingers chopped off by an axe.

Elton and colleagues supported the view that the extraneous details in Petrovich's study were confusing. However, their own presentation of pain as 'disembodied' clearly implies a lack of respect for any broad cultural model of pain. The respondents in this study were men and women from three different groups: 'pain-prone' patients, 'organic' pain patients and a control group. They were given ten seconds between each segment of film to record their responses on seven-point scales. As with the Petrovich study, the analysis is limited, concentrating on significant correlations between variables, but not taking factors such as gender into account. There were no significant differences found between any of the groups, and the authors concluded that, although these types of test do not have much use as a *clinical* measure of pain reactivity, 'they may be useful in determining intercultural differences in responsiveness to pain, and individual differences. When used in conjunction with other methods, they may tap some of the more elusive dimensions of pain' (Elton *et al.* 1983: 30).

Ironically, this was precisely the quality that I was seeking for the kinds of questions I wanted to ask. The vulnerability of pain makes it a 'sensitive' research topic, a term that, as Lee and Renzetti (1990) point out, is often thought to be self-explanatory, although it needs defining carefully. Topics are usually thought to be sensitive because they are controversial in some way, that is they may be threatening to either the researched or the researcher. Any participation in a research project involves the 'costs' of time and possibly inconvenience, but there may also be more unwelcome consequences such as guilt, embarrassment or even the possibility of discovery. Researchers may feel threatened by placing themselves in compromising or dangerous situations, or by experiencing stigmatisation for studying particular topics.

Lee and Renzetti (1990: 512) define four broad areas in which research is likely to be deemed threatening:

1.   Where research intrudes into a private sphere or delves into some deeply personal experience.

2.   Where the study is concerned with deviance and social control.

3.   Where it impinges on vested interests of powerful persons or the exercise of coercion or domination.

4.   Where it deals with things sacred to those being studied which they do not wish to be profaned.

Researching perceptions of pain would seem to fall into the first category, but definitions of the 'private sphere' may vary considerably. Although, by its very nature, pain may become a public concern, it is certainly a 'personal experience' which may be threatening because it is so emotionally charged. One possible reason for overcoming reluctance to discuss these socially 'taboo' topics is the desire for 'catharsis' as there may be relief of disclosure, gains in knowledge or other beneficial effects for participants.

One way to overcome some of these problems is to incorporate vignette techniques into in-depth interviewing. Finch (1987) advocates the use of a hypothetical situation which permits interviewees to define the meaning for themselves and thus:

> Allow[s] for features of the content to be specified, so that the
> respondent is being invited to make normative statements about a set
> of social circumstances, rather than to express his or her 'beliefs' or
> 'values' in a vacuum . . . it acknowledges that meanings are social and
> that morality may well be socially specific.   (Finch 1987: 106)

The method developed in the United States in the late 1960s used *factorial* vignettes used to mimic experiments. A basic story was presented which remained constant but the outcomes were varied, and responses were recorded and analysed in survey fashion (see Lomas Cook 1979; Alves and Rossi 1986). Finch herself used a more complex form of vignette in her study of the public morality of obligations to assist kin. This involved the construction of characters in a story with up to three possible different outcomes. She stresses the flexibility of the technique:

> asking concrete questions about third parties has the effect of
> distancing the issues . . . this seems to make the questions less
> personally threatening, which may be very important when the
> sensitive features of relationships are being explored. It also has the
> effect of breaking away from the limitations imposed by the personal
> experience and circumstances.   (Finch 1987: 111)

Researching sensitive topics raises many issues – methodological, technical, ethical, political and legal. As a result, and as Lee and Renzetti (1990: 513) point out, technical innovation can follow 'in the form of imaginative methodological advances'. A prime consideration of the in-depth interview was to conduct it in a manner that acknowledged the potential vulnerability of the subjects in exposing their feelings about distressing experiences. The use of vignettes could potentially provide a vehicle to explore these experiences 'safely' as well as being extremely valuable in tapping general beliefs. Thus an innovatory use of vignettes incorporating visual imagery was included in an interpretative, phenomenological interview. As this approach appears to be somewhat unique within the literature, its development is described below in detail.

The visual imagery technique

As we have seen, turning to the arts and literature is often recommended as a strategy for better understanding the subjective nature of pain. My own interest in using visual images in order to probe more deeply into beliefs and attitudes about illness and pain emerged initially from a 'lay' appreciation, especially of the relationship between art and society following the work of Berger (1972) and others challenging the exclusivity of 'high culture'. Despite the impact of sociological theories on art history throughout the 1970s and 1980s (particularly Marxist and feminist critiques – see, for example, Fischer 1964; Nochlin 1989; Lippard 1976; Pollock 1982), there have been few reciprocal attempts to enhance social perspectives. Indeed, despite recent challenges to the constitution of knowledge and the focus on issues of cultural representation, there still appears to be a remarkable reluctance to endorse anything but the written word as text. Notable exceptions here include Goffman's (1979) path-breaking *Gender Advertisements* and the subsequent wealth of feminist and cultural analyses of representation in the visual media (Williamson 1978; Fyfe and Law 1988; Bonner *et al.* 1992); also Wex's (1979) photographic work on 'female' and 'male' body language in public space, and Thewelweit's (1987/1989) use of visual imagery in his fascinating two-volume study *Male Fantasies*. More broadly, the recent *The Quick and the Dead: Artists and Anatomy* exhibition provides a particularly good example of the 'meeting of text and image' (Petherbridge 1997). Nevertheless, even when visual images are used, they are seldom displayed without captions or labels.

Within the social sciences, the study of perception has traditionally been embedded in scientific models, with a consequent lack of acknowledgement of the ways in which the social order is represented and endorsed by art, as Wolff pronounces: 'Like society, art is a creation of individual members who, in their turn, are in many ways formed by society' (Wolff 1975: 7). She explores the methodological difficulties of developing a sociology of art, contending that the underpinnings of both positivism and phenomenology lack structural and historical perspectives. This gives rise to problems when implementing the concept of a world-view to demonstrate that a work of art may express the ethos or ideology of a period or particular social group. Wolff suggests a hermeneutic approach to the analysis of imagery, involving the combination of two disparate epistemological enquiries, namely 'the micro-analysis of the individual, phenomenological linguistic experience and the macro- or social knowledge-constitutive determining interests' (1975: 36).

At first glance, as Bourdieu remarks, sociology and art make an 'odd couple'. On the one hand, the artist holds total belief in the uniqueness of their 'gift' or talent, while the sociologist, on the other hand, aims to classify and explain, thereby fragmenting and disturbing the doctrinaire (Bourdieu 1980: 207). Like society, art is the creation of individual members who are themselves socially (trans)formed in the process. Similarly, the appreciation of art itself is not a natural 'God-given' gift, but a socially inculcated disposition; one that is unevenly distributed throughout society, predisposing some to define themselves as 'art lovers' while others are deprived of this privilege (Bourdieu, Dabel and Schnapper 1990). More generally, art provides a powerful medium through which dominant ideas and beliefs about the body and its relationship to the broader social, cultural and political order are reflected and reinforced (Adler and Pointon 1993).

Given the flexibility and versatility of sociological methodology and the developments in qualitative techniques, the use of artistic imagery to probe concepts of pain seemed entirely feasible and subsequently a vignette technique using a series of paired images, instead of stories, was used (see Figures 7–12). I already had a collection from various European art galleries of postcard reproductions of paintings and photographs with pain as a theme. Visits to the National Gallery, the Tate Gallery, the Photographer's Gallery, the Magnum exhibition at the Hayward Gallery, the Museum of Mankind and the Natural History Museum expanded the collection up to thirty postcards, from which a workable selection was then made. As the major focus of the study was gender, I was hoping to portray salient or even 'stereotypical' gendered images of pain (childbirth for women and battle or sports injuries for men).[1] However, despite intensive searching at this time, I was unable to find either a photographic or artistic image of a woman in pain

---

1. These images were found and used in a later study of attendees of a pain clinic (see Bendelow 1996).

in childbirth (the images I found depicted serenity, joy or even ecstasy). None the less, the gendered pairs that emerged seemed to provide complementary contexts (see Figures 8, 9 and 10). Other themes seemed to form natural pairs (Figures 7 and 12) and some of these images also raised other structural issues such as age and race (Figures 8 and 11), which I wanted to include. Nevertheless, acknowledgement must be made of the subjectivity of the final choices, which are influenced by my own definitions and beliefs about pain, and by features of my own background, including my professional training in psychiatry. For instance, 'emotional pain' is a term open to many different interpretations, but which for me personally had no problems as a usable concept. That this is not the case universally is reflected in responses to the material. For example, the use of an image such as *The Lady of Shalott* to symbolise pain was quite mystifying for some people, both respondents and colleagues. Inclusion of that painting was clearly coloured by my own knowledge and interpretation of the story behind the painting. Another complicating factor is that, as emphasised earlier, artistic material, particularly fine art, is highly culturally embedded. The collection of images I used is undoubtedly Eurocentric, and also covers varied timespans, which may serve to distract or influence any responses. Nevertheless, the richness of responses far outweighs any of these dilemmas, as the next section demonstrates.

Responses to visual imagery

In the interview situation, respondents were presented with the six pairs of images, one at a time, without any information about the artist or the background (if desired, this was offered at the end of the sequence), and asked the following:

1. What is happening to the people in the picture?
2. Is anyone in the pictures in pain?
3. Is there more pain in one picture than the other?

Respondents were then shown all the images together and asked the following:

4. Who is in the most pain out of all the images?
5. Who do you identify with most?

Although there was no time limit, respondents were asked to give as immediate a response as possible, and were reassured that there was no right or wrong answer, and that I was not making any judgements about their responses, which were both noted and tape-recorded.

Responses to the images are evaluated here by gathering together and comparing the reactions to each pair of images in turn, and examining these for common themes. The size of the sample made this manageable in practical terms; material gathered in the questionnaires and interviews is drawn on for interpreting individual responses. Second, an assessment is made of the advantages and disadvantages of this exploratory technique as a research tool.

An overview of reactions to the images: common themes

One of the most immediately striking features of the responses is that, despite the diversity of backgrounds of respondents and their different levels of articulation, the content of each pair of images produced very similar responses, and an 'over-arching' view is apparent in each pair. Each pair of images is presented here with a selection of quotes which reflect the 'majority' view or interpretation, even though they may be articulated and expressed in diverse ways. Each pair also gave rise to reactions that were interpreted quite differently, and this 'minority' view is also expressed to try to provide a balanced picture.

PAIR 1

A. *The Sick Child* by Edvard Munch

B. *A Hopeless Dawn* by Frank Bramley

On the whole, picture A is seen to be more concerned with physical illness, and also to be more distressing and conveying pain. The theme of emotional pain is expressed continuously, sometimes with ambivalence, and many of the interpretations of the pictures are concerned with defining the type of pain:

> They don't seem to be in physical pain there, seems to be mental pain. She's sort of, er, that one there that seems to be in bed and the other one holding her hand or something, [A] maybe she's dying – looks like an old sort of Victorian thing.
> *Q: Who's suffering the most?*
> Well, physically her [A] and mentally her [B] because she's giving the impression that if it is old times, then maybe the diet or health isn't very good but she's only contracted what she's got in the last couple of years – maybe cancer or TB or typhoid or whatever it is they catch, she's only had it in the past couple of years but she looks like she's had a hard life all along and whatever she's got left she's still going to have it so . . . pain, actual pain she seems to be suffering worst but

A.

B.

Figure 7: Pair 1
A. *The Sick Child* by Edvard Munch
1907, © Munch Museum/Munch–Ellingsen Group, BONO, Oslo, DACS, London 2000

B. *A Hopeless Dawn* by Frank Bramley
1888, © Tate Gallery, London 1999

she seems to have broken down, she seems to have broken down –
they seem to have got me, the bastards, there's nothing I can do
about it – it's funny really . . . M1

In [A] grief and stress and misery – that's what I immediately focus on
– it seems to be that the woman at the bedside is expressing greater
grief than the patient – my immediate feeling is that she's the
daughter and she is looking almost with a calm expression of
detachment, almost a feeling of slight satisfaction on her face . . .
Then I look at the other one . . . it's a rough night outside, perhaps
they're waiting for the fishermen to come home but to me it's too
simple an expression of pain and grief – I can't feel my way into that,
to me it's the other one which for me is the much more moving one
which is much more baffling. M10

Respondents included personal feelings and experiences in their
interpretations:

Very emotive, reminds me a lot of my own illness – the figures in
both must be mothers and daughters and they remind me of my
mother and the care she gave me, how distressed she was . . . [A] is
most distressing – [B] looks more as if her boyfriend has left her or
something – I don't mean that's not painful but the other one looks
as if she's very ill, dying . . . F1

The one that gets me more is [A] – it's a deeper sort of pain – [B] just
looks as if she's been dumped by someone – a lover or something and
she's a bit upset, very upset but [A] is obviously suffering – the child is
looking after the mother, there's more emotional pain. Well, they're
both emotional pains but [A] is far more extreme – it makes me feel
sadder. F6

That [A] is more painful . . . it's strange, I was talking to my sister
about when my mother died the other day and she was very, my
sister was talking about how she felt nursing my mother through
cancer, being in pain, so that really makes it stand out . . . M6

Two men and one woman thought that pain was not portrayed in
the images.

A.

B.

Figure 8:   Pair 2
A. *Famine in India 1951*
Werner Bischof/Magnum
Photos

B. *Old man with his head in his hands, 'At eternity's gate'* by Vincent van Gogh
1882, © Amsterdam, Van Gogh Museum (Vincent van Gogh Foundation)

PAIR 2

A. *Famine in India 1951* by Werner Bischof

B. *Old man with his head in his hands, 'At eternity's gate'* by
   Vincent van Gogh

The reactions to these images again revel a common theme. The choice
of these particular pictures was influenced by the fact that, as well as portraying gender, they also raised issues of age, class and race. Of all these social
characteristics, the main focus was on race and class, unanimously seen
in the context described above, as symbolic of 'third world' deprivation:

> I think it's very difficult to know in the rich West what it's like
> to have to beg for bread to know what those feelings are. I think if we
> are reduced to begging in this country our feelings are quite different
> from people who beg in a society where a much bigger percentage of
> the population begs, where it's much more acceptable than it is here .
> . . I mean one can be outraged that she shouldn't jolly well have to
> but that's making a judgement on a society that one imperfectly
> understands though I wouldn't wish to sanctify begging on the streets
> – it's never an acceptable way that human beings should live but it's
> very difficult to sort that out – it excites pity. F7

The man's plight is seen as private and personalised, whereas the
woman is seen as representative of a universal suffering, the public 'pain'
of the underdeveloped world.

> This one [B] conjures up the pain of the individual whereas this one
> [A] is the more harrowing picture-graph and it makes you aware of
> the plight of people. Maybe, not for me personally, you'd think it was
> less of the plight of an individual, you'd think more of a people, a
> group of people but also it can re-identify the fact that there are
> individuals when you talk about problems such as famine or, it could
> be anything whereas the drawing – if you know a bit about Van Gogh
> it picks up the artist's palm, a man creating pain, in inner turmoil – I
> can probably relate to that more but I suppose if I'm honest this is the
> more moving because there's something more contrived about an
> artist, especially when he's a famous artist . . . M4

> Well, I think there's suffering in this picture [A] but it's . . . perhaps
> one projects ideas on to these things, that's what I'm doing – but it's
> more like a universal suffering rather than a personal pain. I know
> that kind of picture quite well and I could go on for hours . . . But the
> second one [B], I don't know whether this man is thinking or whether
> he is actually suffering. Because of the nature of the subject you've

given me I'm biased – I'm looking more at the drawing than I am looking at the human figure who could be possibly crying, possibly thinking but it's more about pain than [A] – that doesn't equal for me again, pain as such. Universally maybe yes, but it's not personalised, it's more universal suffering, that's what I see. M8

Strangely enough, [B] is more, um, sort of hopeful – [A] looks like Ethiopia, India or something, the starving . . . there's not much light at the end of that tunnel. But [B] a grown man crying, he obviously looks quite old – I don't know I think it makes me sadder – it's something that's happened to him that's more emotionally painful, it's different. But this is sort of more environmental – what's happening around is explaining – that's what's affecting her. But it's probably worse really. F6

Whether or not the content of the pictures are defined as pain, the 'public' nature of the plight of the woman appears to act to reduce empathy for her; even though there is a consensus that she is probably suffering more, his personal grief seems to produce more immediate sympathy:

I feel upset looking at him – that could be me when I get old, I don't want to end up like that. He's probably fought in the war, all sorts of things but just to end up in pain, old, alone – he's probably got cancer or something . . . I know she's probably even worse off, she could be starving even but I'm much more sorry for him. M2

The man is in anguish, what he's going through is certainly not pleasant but it's a personal anguish whereas the woman – it should be more shocking – I don't know if it's because it's a photograph but I don't know also whether it's pain – it could be death, loss, torture, something happening in the body but it's not personal. Both represent different things. F8

There are responses that do not consider these images to convey pain as such:

They're more a familiar picture of despair more than pain – they're more of hopelessness . . . both of them . . . M9

The man is angry – he's lost everything through his own fault, he's lost all of it – it's like an omen that happens every ten or twenty years. It's possibly grief but also despair, it's not physical pain but emotional stress. For her, after many years of anguish maybe there's some hope – the person taking the picture represents hope. M7

PAIR 3

A. *The Lady of Shalott* by John William Waterhouse

B. *Melancholy I* by Edvard Munch

This pair created a strong emotional reaction, in that the majority of the sample did not think the images portrayed pain at all, although there was a much more sympathetic response to image B:

> That's quite a stark sort of picture [B] – I do think it's horrible, the black and white . . . it's not conveying anything, just a sort of incredible desolation. With her there is suffering in her face, not agony but not much joy, it's a romantic sadness but it's preferable to him, he's in more pain. F5

> I hate the romantic painters . . . [A] she looks like she's in liver failure [laughs] – it's not painful, it's like a Flake ad almost, like a panda, bashed round the eyes maybe but she's asking for it going round like that [B] . . . but that one shows real depression – that's the loneliness bit but not like pain . . . although I suppose if you feel really low and really sent to Coventry by your peers that must be painful. That makes me feel sadness . . . but that one [A] just makes me feel slightly sickly sentimental. M2

> No, no, they don't do anything for me – it's just despair, it's not pain, maybe you see them differently. M9

Even if the woman in picture A is seen to be in pain, it is seen as the pain of 'romantic love', which is portrayed as being rather ridiculous, not to be taken seriously, and certainly not 'real' pain. Some respondents even indicate a narcissistic self-inflicted quality, whereas the loneliness and isolation of the male figure (B) is seen as a more valid form of suffering:

> If you had to die, that's the way to go.
> Q: Is there any pain?
> Emotional pain, yes. There was enough emotional pain for the Lady of Shalott to end her life and for him, there's pain, a heartbreaking sort of pain. My sympathies are more with him – I don't like martyrdom really or maybe I'm just not in a very sympathetic mood. F6

> Q: Is she in pain?
> Yes but possibly quite enjoying it. I know that sounds very cynical and I wouldn't have said that twenty years ago, I'm sure, but yes, she

A.

B.

Figure 9:   Pair 3.
A. *The Lady of Shalott* by John William Waterhouse
1888, © Tate Gallery, London

B. Melancholy I by Edvard Munch
1896 Photo: © Munch Museum (Svein Andersen/Sidsel de Jong) 2000
Copyright: © Munch Museum/Munch-Ellingsen Group, BONO, Oslo, DACS 2000

probably feels she is but sort of pain and love and beauty are sort of all intermingled. The second one, I really had to look hard at to see him, which if it were an autobiographical thing would show that the person had very low self-esteem. Even now the person is saying it looks so hopeless, it's almost like a sense of him merging with the surroundings. He could just be thoughtful, when I look closely at his face – again he makes me think of somebody withdrawing because they can't face themselves or outside. I think I'd choose him in that he looks more like a real-life person. F4

Only two of the respondents appeared to empathise or feel there was any genuine plight in picture A, and both these respondents named picture A as the one they most identified with:

This girl here, it's hard to say, she's a lady that was in love or something, she's all forlorn-looking, isn't she? She's in pain, she looks as if she's heartbroken. With this I can't make out that – is this an ocean, a water or what, somebody drowning with their hands up – oh, when I have it close enough now I can see his face – he seems to be, um, right down and out, doesn't he, as if he is tormented – there's something really worrying him, isn't there? I think she's bad – she's heartbroken, or she's lost someone so she'd be more likely to do away with herself – I'm not saying this gentleman, he's not in pain but I think she's worse, I feel very sorry for both of them but she's like me, she's lost her man. F9

She is showing the pain of an inadequate world – a melancholic love of life as known by her, a more esoteric life. He is really black and white – lonely, empty – a black snake in a human body. There is no emotional comfort there whatsoever, I used to feel like that in the mental hospital, I'd rather be the woman. M7

A.

B.

Figure 10:   Pair 4
A. *Saint Sebastian* by Gerrit van Honthorst
1590, © National Gallery, London

B. *The Broken Column* by Frida Kahlo
1944, Collection of Dolores Olmedo, Mexico City

PAIR 4

A. *Saint Sebastian* by Gerrit van Honthorst

B. *The Broken Column* by Frida Kahlo

For the first time the images actually depict physical pain being inflicted on the subjects. This invokes mixed reactions – of fear, of revulsion, and, when viewed initially, A is seen to be in more pain than B.

> Ah, that's in a foreign land, isn't it? He reminds me of Jesus . . . and her Good God . . . this is really bad but she doesn't look in pain – she looks forlorn-looking, not wild looking, but she seems to be in another world, you know . . . He's in the most pain, like Jesus on the cross, it's terrible, really terrible . . . F9

> Well, I don't know what he's done to get all those things stuck in him, he doesn't look in pain but he must be, in great pain. She's not a real person, it's probably worse but she don't look real to me. M9

> She's been tortured into confessing something like witchcraft and he looks like he's obviously been tied up to be killed but he's obviously been humiliated first – there's one through his leg and one through his arm so they've obviously made him suffer that pain first and that one in the stomach would make him suffer whereas this one is aimed right at the heart – it looks like he's been made to suffer, the two of them have but she probably suffered the worst – with all them pins and that she's obviously been made to feel terrible pain – in some of the things they did to people, I've read up on it. M1

Sado-masochistic themes were invoked by various respondents, some of whom found the images disturbing, others less so:

> Both these two are having incredibly painful things done to them but they don't seem real, they seem like concoctions or creations, especially the woman, she's like a robot. They conjure up visions of acupuncture to me – which may not necessarily hurt much at all. The nails in her breasts quite disturb me because they do look realistic but otherwise it's just like an intellectualised appreciation of pain. I suppose if I chose I would say he's in more pain because it must be pretty excruciating having arrows through your arms and things, but he's not showing pain, it's not at all emotional but fascinating in a cold way. F1

> It's funny because when I see pictures like this I can look at it very dispassionately and be worried about the poor guy's spleen or something but . . . it makes you wonder why on earth anybody would

want to have that picture on their wall – not that I don't feel sorry for San Sebastien. As for the other one, well that's just weird, that is. It's somehow deliberately – well, both of them are pictures of deliberately inflicted physical pain, either by somebody else or by themselves, I'm not sure who would stick drawing pins in this poor woman but I find them a real turn-off – I don't understand it, it doesn't play a part in any part of my life or of my relationships . . . this one disturbs me more but it's very hard to say because if she gets some sort of kick sticking drawing pins into herself then it's not necessarily more painful than having arrows stuck into you. F10

This is San Sebastien – there is almost something like a narcissism of pain. People sometimes talk in terms of sado-masochism in relation to this subject and so I'm not very surprised that there's an element of sado-masochism in the other picture – there is horror in both of them but I have a feeling of almost some faint pornography – the eroticism, the mixture of pain, pleasure, bondage suggested by the bands around her waist – it's a nasty picture but also I must say I find it faintly attractive, compelling – images of crucifixion. But there's something sort of sado-masochistic about it that I don't respond to or if I do I'm perhaps ashamed to acknowledge. The San Sebastien – the beauty of the body, the face, the painter has enjoyed putting the arrows and the blood on the body – it's quite disconcerting . . . M10

The San Sebastien, I don't know if that's pain, it's almost sexual, it's about something else . . . he's too prettily poised. As for her, she's not a real woman, it's an image of a woman . . . neither of them are about pain, they are symbols of something else. F8

The lack of expression in both the faces obscures the reactions of many of the respondents, resulting in a 'distancing' of feelings, sometimes attributed to the artistic style:

This is . . . is frightening [B] but it feels more like a yogi in its feeling – the idea that you're seeing inside of a person with a broken column inside being held together with straps – a broken landscape too. It's trying to talk about pain but my feeling would be to make it much simpler. [A] This one with the arrows is more, the idea of pain is in seeing the arrow coming out with the blood, there's a certain feeling of thud about it but at the same time you kind of feel slightly divorced from it, partly due to the lighting – it feels like a theatre stage set so in a way it gets you in the pit of the stomach but you don't necessarily think in terms of pain in terms of the picture, you're more thinking in terms of what the spirit is doing, in terms of what it's about – I think that is the purpose of the picture. My feeling is that it is trying to talk about a certain type of pain – more like an intellectual exercise. In a way I'd feel like the picture would be enough if I just had one or two of the details – I just feel that the body in itself is sitting there, it seems impervious – I would feel that it should be reacting more. I mean in both cases you would feel there should be something more – when you see someone die, I mean it's not a necessarily peaceful occupation . . . that passivity, acceptance. Definitely this feels like a mantra, a Hindu interpretation of life in which you're really passing through to another stage of life. I suppose there's more pain in this one in the way you can read it in. M3

Neither of them particularly, well, they're both symbolic in their own way – I mean it conjures up feelings but not emotions. The pain from the one on the right [B] is about what you should be feeling and you will feel but you won't . . . well, I think that it represents pain but I don't think you can feel it from that image but you are aware of what it means – the pain is made real. It's symbolism, when you're not actually feeling it in your gut but you feel it in your head . . . The other one is . . . is too clean, you know what I mean, it might as well be done like with an airbrush. Maybe if you're really religiously inclined then any image of Christ's suffering is going to stir . . . but

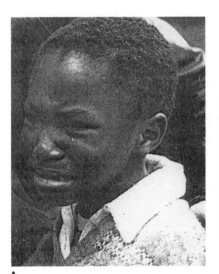

A.   **B.**

Figure 11: Pair 5
A. Scene from a London playground
Network Photographers 1987

B. *Hungary 1947*
Werner Bischof/Magnum Photos

there are so many really harrowing, stirring images that this is not comparable. Again it might conjure up his suffering in your mind but not in your heart. If I had to say, I think [B] is more evocative. M4

PAIR 5

A. *Scene from a London Playground*, Network Photographers

B. *Hungary 1947* by Werner Bischof

This pair of images gave rise to the most immediate emotional reactions, usually of sympathy or pity. Most of the subjects claimed to feel upset or distressed by looking at them:

> At first sight they both have a big impact and make me feel upset but I don't know why they're crying – I would think that the black child is in more pain, it seems more intense and there may be racist implications there whereas the other child may be upset because it's been sick or something. F1

> They're both in pain, they're equally upset and both very sad, both suffering. They stir much more emotion in me than anything else I've seen. F3

> The black child on the left is in far more pain, he's in agony whereas the child on the right is sort of dazed. They're both equally as sad but the black child has more pain. F8

> Well, definitely the one on the left [A], it just appears more real, more authentic, more hurt. This one might affect people because he's a more beautiful child or because he hasn't got the grimace of pain on his face, he just appears as if he's just stopped crying but the realism of what he's going through, the pain, anguish . . .
> Q. *Does it actually make you feel anything?*
> Yes, it does, it does. Just that one not the other, I mean he's cute but this one is really in trouble . . . M4

> The one on the left especially [A], the expression on the face, which is what we are conditioned to reflect – there is more suffering – there is some in the one on the right but there is more in the one on the left . . . looking at these pictures, they're quite strong because I don't see him with a nail in his foot and I don't see him necessarily with his bottom smacked – although maybe more there – I see much more despair there than I do here but then maybe that's photographs – you show me a photo of him in this much despair and I'd say yes – or reverse it. Certainly the one on the left, anyway. M8

[A] has more immediate impact . . . he's crying, he's out of control and to me that's the deeper pain – more immediate, more physical, his head, his body is out of control and the attempt to comfort him – the hand of the adult – I don't know whether it being white is relevant or not but there's no reaching him, he's sobbing uncontrollably. There's a grave, almost stoic look about the other, of course one is moved by both of them because one hates to see children in distress but I feel more pity for the one on the left. On the other hand it's probable the one on the left will probably be laughing and joking whereas the one on the right will – his melancholy will probably be a more long-term one because he's looking out so steadily at life – looking out so clearly and strongly and sternly – it's almost philosophical . . . M10

However, there were three responses that were very different from the others – from the two oldest people in the sample, one male and one female and the youngest man:

Well, he's been told not to play with his white school-children friends and the boy on the right is the boy that he's been refused to play with and he's having a few tears . . . it's like race relations but it's not pain, just childish tears and having disagreement or being told not to play with each other. F3

You don't take children crying so seriously so much now, it's become a bit of a cliché. This one [A] it seems more like he's genuinely crying about something.
Q: *Right, so what's happened to this one?*
Oh, he's had his sweeties taken away or something. M2

Yes, but children cry. Small children can be absolutely heartbreaking for the lack of another Smartie – you can't always take it so seriously, tremendous tears, upset – they don't look in pain. M5

In other words, there is a notion that children's pain need not be taken seriously in comparison to that of adults.

A.

B.

Figure 12: Pair 6
A. *Two Followers of Cadmus Devoured by a Dragon* by Cornelis van Haarlem
1624, © National Gallery, London

B. *Judith Decapitating Holofernes* by Artemisia Gentileschi (detail)
c. 1618, Uffizi Gallery, Florence

PAIR 6

A. *Two Followers of Cadmus Devoured by a Dragon* by Cornelis van Haarlem

B. *Judith Decapitating Holofernes* by Artemisia Gentileschi

The final pair again depict gory, violent images, and produce some responses of horror and refusal to look at the images.

> I don't know what to say about these – they're both so revolting I don't even want to have to look at them. F10

> Oh good gracious, I can't see them properly, thank goodness. My immediate reaction is sort of bewilderment but . . . tell the library to give you some different pictures . . . F3

> Oh good God, that's a sacrilegious thing, isn't it, they're cutting his head off, good God, and they're cutting his throat – this is terrible what they've done, this is the worst one, they're crucifying him, cutting his throat and it makes me shudder – that one does as well but that is worse – it upsets all your system as soon as I look at it . . . F9

Again, there was a process of 'distancing' from the horror portrayed in the images. Discussion of the artistic style was often used to create this distance, by employing an analytical, more intellectualised response, which serves to reduce the possible distress:

> I just can't imagine why anyone would want to paint pictures like these . . . That's just like fantasy to me – I don't like it but I just kind of accept it and I suppose that's my first impression of it. Both those scenes are a bit unreal – my initial impression is almost sort of annoyance that someone would create a picture like that. I think that this one is sort of beyond pain but the other one shows a sort of desolation. F5

> Very unpleasant – like something out of a horror movie. There doesn't seem to be a lot of pain in there – it's gruesome basically. There's an inevitability about it – that expression is a lot more, um, pained – but the expressions on their faces – we're going to kill you, so there, so you may as well just lie back and enjoy and he isn't struggling much, it doesn't seem – there's a childlike quality about it like young children pulling off the legs of ants and frogs and things, not caring. And the dragons – obviously they did something naughty but of the two that is the least – none of them are pleasant but I like dragons. F6

Bloody hell, that's one way of getting rid of the husband, isn't it? Well, this one [A] makes me think of those sort of films – like Friday the 13th or Nightmare on Elm Street. Well, this is probably some sort of devilish thing, something very unholy and evil – you can see someone's had their head ripped off – that sort of thing makes me think at times I wonder what sort of mind people have got to – er, dream that sort of thing up . . . For this one [B], I feel that could be me, it could happen to anyone but this sort of thing doesn't seem real, it's more like Spielberg or something, I don't identify with that because I don't like that sort of film, I don't like people getting killed, I don't like those pictures, it doesn't do anything for me at all but that one I don't see as being real, it's more been created for the camera or the painting. This one I can familiarise with that more because that is real, has gone on, did go on and still goes on now – it looks like he's been asleep and they've come in and caught him by surprise, by the time he's realised what's happened it's too late, he can't do nothing to save himself so I feel more pity for him, you know, make sure you lock the kitchen up . . . they could have killed him for a number of reasons, judging by the look on their faces it could have been mother and daughter, he could have been a murderer or a rapist, anything like that. I think that's a bit sick really. M1

It is difficult to portray pain as such, isn't it – you can put it in terms of theatre which this is . . . That's meant to be George and the Dragon in the background, I think. I imagine this is meant to be a lady but it may be a man. I mean that has a feeling of the hope behind the disaster. This is more ruthless, it looks like an illustration from the Bible – one of these final solutions. I'm afraid you have to say that because he's been caught in his sleep, there's more pain involved here. At the same time, this looks like a corpse, this bit – but it doesn't feel like pain as such. This has more – you see that face, it could have been taken from a cadaver or something. It turns your gut but not in the sense of pain. I suppose I could say I'm surprised it takes two ladies to get a bloke while he's asleep. There is a certain amount of pain in that face but it's more pain of surprise than pain of pain. You can feel from this that the person is obviously rich but there's no real clues to why, I suppose it's revenge. M3

Where on earth did you get these? I think that's the worst one actually, getting murdered by two women, unless they're trying to help him commit suicide! He must have been a terrible husband or father, or whatever . . . This one is pure fantasy, very unpleasant but that's worse because it's more probable. Presumably there'd be a lot of physical pain there but not a lot of emotional pain but there obviously there's been a lot of angst about what the relationship is, unless they're female burglars. But it looks as if they're fed up with this guy who's led their lives quite a – and they're taking it out on him. M6

At the end of the sequence, respondents were asked to look at all the images together and, if possible, to choose which person was in the most pain and which person they identified with most. The crying child (Pair 5, A) was given the highest overall rating for 'most pain' and was the most popular male choice, whereas *The Sick Child* (Pair 1, A) was preferred by females. Picture A in Pair 5 was again the choice of identification for both men and women, but equal ranking was given by females only to *A Hopeless Dawn* (Pair 1, B) and by males only to *Melancholy* (Pair 3, B).

Links between the public and the private: using visual imagery in data collection

Obviously, using artistic material, and particularly the range of material included in this selection, is complicated, not least because of the problems of interpretation of cultural meaning. Preliminary discussions about using this type of material had raised the issue that some people might relate to artistic representations better than others – in other words there would be a social class advantage in that the higher social classes would be more familiar with the materials. In fact, given the responses from this sample, this would not seem to be the case. Obviously, there were differences in the styles of articulation, and people with an artistic background or knowledge discussed the images more analytically, to the extent that they sometimes became inappropriately diverted by discussing technical styles (for instance, the merits of photographs over paintings or vice versa). It appeared that the less the respondent knew about the picture, or art in general, the less contrived was the response. Comparisons were often made with television programmes, popular novels or media advertising, and the quality of responses was very rich and philosophically profound, as the quotes illustrate. An important methodological issue is that using images enables the subject-matter to which respondents are asked to react to be standardised – the images stay the same, whereas questions may alter in context or expression from interview to interview. A second important methodological point is that the use of images gives rise to an immediate response, and does not necessarily require a high level of articulation, although obviously how people talk affects what they say.

On the whole there was enormous enthusiasm to look at and discuss visual images. Even the subjects who felt that the exercise was pointless when it was first explained to them (Suni, F3 and Bob, M9) did not refuse to take part, and made appropriate and relevant contributions. The only person who was unable to use the material at all was Helen (F2), as her eyesight was impaired by her accident, and she was unable to decipher many of the scenes, but still attempted to do so with my assistance. Marie (F9), who was unable to read or write, cooperated enthusiastically in the exercise, which she would have been unable to do with text.

Although in need of methodological refinement, this technique has enormous potential and the resulting richness of the data justifes practical difficulties in presenting material of this nature. Everybody in the sample participated in some form, and most respondents claimed to enjoy the exercise; some even claimed to find it therapeutic. This was especially so of the subjects who had experienced traumatic treatments involving hospitalisation (for example, Peter (M10), who had undergone radical surgery for cancer, and Rachel (F10), who had several operations on her leg after a road traffic accident), or severe emotional disturbance (for example, Michael (M7), who had received long-term treatment for paranoid schizophrenia, Tim (M4), who was experiencing constant debilitating anxiety attacks, and Jane (F7), who had experienced a long period of distress and despair due to her son's mental illness). All these respondents expressed the view that contemplating the plight of the people in the images somehow helped to put their own dilemmas into perspective, and gave them an opportunity to 'cope' with the feelings that their own personal events had thrown up for them. In the same way that Finch (1987) demonstrates how the vignette technique provides a form of 'desensitisation' – an acceptable way of talking about the private in public – many respondents claimed that it was a relief to take part in the imagery exercise after having revealed in some depth their own 'pain stories', and to contemplate something that was happening to someone else. This desensitisation was mutually beneficial, from the point of view of 'the burden of interviewing'. As can be seen from the case studies, many of the 'pain stories' were extremely harrowing to listen to, so the chance to turn to something more distancing was personally relieving.

This study is not claiming to be scientific or even clinical. The use of interviews and visual imagery is about as far removed from the traditional studies of pain perceptions which inflict noxious stimuli to demonstrate psychophysical laws as one can get. Nevertheless, this exploration of pain beliefs and concepts has, I hope to show, some value in widening our understandings of complexities of pain. As a practising medic, Trisha Greenhalgh points out: 'appreciating the narrative nature of illness experience and the intuitive and subjective aspects of clinical competence does not require the practitioner to reject one iota the principles of clinical epidemiology' (Greenhalgh 1998: 247). Moreover, this study is concerned with widening our understanding of pain beyond the medical and the clinical, to conceptualise pain sociologically and contextualise it as part of everyday life.

chapter 5

'It's not *real* pain':
emotions versus sensations

In setting up the interviews, the respondents were asked whether they were willing to go into more detail about some of the issues in the questionnaires. As up to six months had elapsed since their completion, recall as to the contents of the questionnaire varied considerably, with some people having no memory of it whatsoever, whereas for others the subject appeared to hold great importance and the questionnaire responses were remembered accurately. The interview began by recalling the questionnaire and asking for more detail about the most painful experience that the respondent could remember. In each case, this gave rise to a 'pain story', the length of which varied considerably. In relating their experience, every person without exception talked about their feelings while recalling the relevant episode and/or incident(s).

The theme of physical versus emotional pain and the separation or interlinking of those two was universally explored, often without my prompting, although I did explicitly ask, if it had not already arisen, whether the interviewee thought that there was such a thing as 'emotional pain'. At this point in the interview a sequence of visual images was introduced, aiming to explore further social perceptions and beliefs about pain. The final part of the interview centred around the questionnaire responses to gender differences and pain perception, and asked the respondents to explain the reasons for their particular responses. Other possible social factors were also probed if they had not yet been mentioned spontaneously – specifically ethnicity, class and age. Finally, interviewees were asked if there were any other factors that they considered important.

The whole interview, including the imagery sequence, was of an in-depth, informal and semi-structured nature, lasting on average for one hour for both men and women. However, some interviews were much longer, the longest being four hours. All the interviews were tape-recorded (unless the interviewees said that they did not want this) and transcribed, and manual notes were also taken. For the analysis stage of the research, the word-processed transcripts were manually 'cut and pasted' into various themes. Due to the size of the sub-sample, it was possible to assimilate all the material in an immediately accessible manner. For example, in the case of the imagery, the relevant quotes were pasted around each pair of images, forming a 'poster' which was then hung on the wall and studied. A similar technique was employed with the rest of the interview data, which was divided into themes. The main themes followed from the two major 'findings' of the questionnaire, summarised as follows:

1.   Most people believed either that women have a superior capacity to men for coping with pain, or that there are no gender differences: a minority said that men were better at coping with pain. When asked why this was so, the female reproductive role was consistently used to explain this notion.

2.   Analysis of the questionnaire data showed that men were significantly less inclined to think that the emotional component of pain perception had any importance.

In this chapter, extensive quotations are used from the interview respondents. The first research issue is raised by exploring the role of emotions in the definitions and experiences of pain. It was hypothesised earlier that the Cartesian 'split' between mind and body poses difficulties for conceptualising pain, as the primary emphasis is on the *nociceptive* or sensory qualities. Although most people in the questionnaire survey defined their worst experience of pain largely in physical terms, emotions were seen to play a part in the process, a gendered notion weighted towards females. By analysing the accounts of experiences of the most painful events of their lives, this chapter explores how the respondents define, and subsequently build up, belief systems about pain.

The conceptualisation of pain

I think you can experience pain on a spiritual level, a mental spiritual level – on a physical level and an emotional level. And although they are holistically one, I would separate them. So if I was a doctor and somebody was suffering from mental pain which was then coming out of the body through things like arthritis or who knows – then that would need a course of treatment and I would say 'Oh, you're in pain, take this tablet' but if it's spiritual anguish it would need another treatment, emotional the same thing – you'd need love. We all need love, we all need care, we all need everything . . . M8

An important aim of using in-depth interviews was to try to 'deconstruct' the mind/body dualism that permeates more clinical approaches to the assessment of pain. In the interview, respondents were asked to describe the most painful experiences of their lives. The following quotes from these 'pain stories' provide vivid illustrations of the complexities involved in talking about pain. Pain was discussed not only in emotional as well as physical terms, but included spiritual, philosophical and existential notions. A closer examination of the taxonomy reveals how the terms *mental, emotional* and *psychological* were used repeatedly and interchangeably, as the following examples show:

Pain itself – it's quite hard to remember *physical* pain – I think probably *mental* pain is the worst – it's hard to say and I can't remember what I put down but I think *mental* pain is worse than *physical* – the *physical* is hard to remember, it goes but the *mental* stays there. M1

No, it isn't just a *physical* thing – it's the way you think about what happens – of course it's *psychological* in that respect and how you think it's going to affect you or not. I mean the worst pain I've witnessed is with my wife having the children and that's something which is a much longer-term thing happening, sort of twenty-four hours on the go. I mean something like what happened to me – a blood infection in the leg – you can put it outside yourself basically in a way, chop it off . . . but not in the case of having a child – it's something you have to see through to the end. In the case of bereavement the time span is longer so the shock wears off and pain gets much longer and larger in that case – so I suppose that's the most fundamental case [of emotional pain] I can think of. Though there's also *emotional* pain in the things you bring up in yourself and discover about yourself and the angst you have, so there's a lot of *emotional* stress in that sense. M3

You see I've not suffered *physically* that much – I don't know if I'd even say I'd suffered *emotionally* – I mean, life is incredibly painful, it's perverse in a way. I know I put that the worst pain I'd experienced would be an *emotional* pain which for me is as valid as other types of pain – I always feel that *physical* pain gets all the attention. I'm not saying the two aren't related but for me I think the most painful

experience if you qualify pain, *emotional* or *physical*, was when my
mother died and I'm still not over that. I don't think you can
articulate pain, I don't think you can find words for *physical* more
than *emotional* pain, I can't find the words . . . ache? I think doctors
should do more work on their language, like what's been done for
children like 'I've got a headache in my tummy' type thing. I think
it's very very hard to find words to express that pain and it's also hard
knowing who to express it to. F8

Everyone in the interview sample acknowledged or made reference
to the existence of 'emotional pain' as a concept, with many respondents
expressing the view that it had the potential to be equal to, or worse than,
physical pain:

I don't know, in some ways it might be easier to be in *physical* pain
than *mental* pain, especially like with people with schizophrenia,
they're often described as being in *mental* pain, aren't they but usually
it's a *physical* thing, there's more chance that the doctor or someone
can cure . . . M6

It's very *psychological* pain – if you don't think about it and take your
mind off it, it will go away or it's not as bad. So if I burn myself now,
I just sort of run it under a tap or read a book or go out, or ring up
someone, I don't think about it . . . *emotional* pain is something that
I've felt quite a lot – in a way I think it's worse than *physical* pain –
that's tangible and you know what's causing it and you can put your
finger on it – well, it hurts there, that's the reason but *emotional* pain
– I mean, I don't think anyone can explain why human beings have
emotions. But because people are capable of loving a great deal,
hating a great deal – if someone you love does something nasty out
of spite, well, that can be worse than any *physical* pain. F6

The responses indicate that there may be a level of stigma, in the
form of increased personal vulnerability, attached to revealing emotional
or psychological pain, and that this appears to be the case for men more
than women. Pain with an easily demonstrable pathological cause, super-
ficially at least, would seem to have more respectability and authenticity:

Of course there is *mental* pain as well but only in its *true* sense pain is
physical – I mean, they're not the same thing – I mean, there's *mental*
pain and there's *physical* pain but they're not the same thing – I
mean, the pain that I've known has been purely *physical* sort of
things. I mean the other sort of pain comes through problems but it's
not related to the *physical* part. I suppose the few times I've been in
jail I would say it's painful but not *physically* so . . . M7

Emotional pain, *emotional* pain, I'm sure I've experienced it but
I don't know how to put it into semantics really. It's not the same
as the type of pain in my hand. In that period I could go to sleep
without pain in my mind and wake up – it'd be the first thing I'd
register when I woke up, you know what I mean, that's how serious
the pain was whereas *emotional* pain – I can't put my finger on what
it is but maybe it's a disturbance – a disturbance of the mind which
causes you to feel depressed for no reason or full of anxiety for no
reason, or incapable or impotent or all those things, for no apparent
reason, maybe that's pain. But to me, I've experienced those things
but I don't let them get to me . . . the actual term exists, doesn't it, so
I don't want to fight against the fact that people can be in *emotional*
hurt. You know, 'Are you hurt by this situation – yes, I'm very hurt',
but then how do you measure that against other hurts? M8

Maybe *physical* pain has more legitimation. Now that I'm trying to
measure or find the words for *emotional* pain, I'm not saying it's not
to be taken seriously because people get psychosomatic pains from
depression like headaches, real aches. I don't get any of those things,
I don't think I do. But then maybe the headache I had last month
was an *emotional* pain! M5

The women in the sample were equally likely to make the same
emotional/physical distinctions, but provided more holistic overviews, and
were more able to acknowledge their emotional vulnerabilities:

Emotions are definitely crucial to *physical* sensations of pain – when
I can step back from what's going on and detach myself – when
I can recognise that I'm more than this body that's going through
its process in its own way. The body has a strong self-righting
mechanism that when I can detach from it, I can let it work itself out,
it can balance itself. I don't need to take painkillers but then also if
you are in extreme pain and you don't have a strong enough sense of
your own being as apart from your body then it can just compound
it. I have become interested in consciousness through this and I
practise meditation – I think that an awareness is essential, not only
for the health of the body but of the mind and the *emotions*. F5

I hate the hierarchy of pain where one pain will be treated with
sincerity and seriousness and other pains are vindicated as not being
important, so I'm not sure on that one. I do think, though I've got no
evidence for it really, it's a lot to do with culture and what's allowed
to be expressed when and where, what's socially acceptable, and in
my experience, mental illness is bottom of the pile. F8

The relative informality and personal contact of the interview appeared to broaden the consideration of experiences that could be defined as pain. Some respondents completely changed their classification of worst pain from questionnaire to interview, from something physical to an emotional or psychological condition. For instance, Tim (M4) had indicated origin-ally that his worst experience of pain had been of a toothache, but as the interview progressed, it emerged that he was experiencing something that was ultimately much more distressing (see case study, p. 100). He stressed that these experiences of 'emotional pain' were worse than anything physical he could imagine, and saw them as a form of torture.

Similarly, as the interview with Jane (F7) progressed, she became increasingly confiding and vulnerable. Jane is a highly articulate 47-year-old woman who is a successful fundraiser for a charity and who describes herself as 'white, English, middle-class owner-occupier, living with my accountant husband and two grown-up children'. In the questionnaire she had, almost apologetically, claimed to have had an uneventful life, her most painful experience being a back injury as a teenager, from which she quickly recovered. But as the interview progressed, another story emerged and she became saddened and serious, relating an account of a problem-atic relationship with her son. She felt that he had always been 'a difficult child', unlike her daughter, but after he reached the age of 16 she found his behaviour impossible. He had become withdrawn and anti-social, and eventually turned to drug-taking and attempted suicide. Five years later, helped by psychotherapy for herself as well as her son, she feels she can accept that he will never be part of the 'mainstream' as she sees it, but thinks it to be the most painful episode of her life. In a frank exchange, she revealed that part of the pain still revolves around whether she is really concerned for him, or about judgements on her motherhood.

> Now I don't worry about him. I think what caused a lot of the pain was the worry about him and, if I'm honest, the worry of what other people would think about me because of his behaviour and I think there is an element of that in all parenting and it took me a long time to stand up to authority – to say, well, that's the way he is, you know, and not to worry, to shed some of the responsibility – I don't feel answerable. It has certainly been worse than any physical experience but then, apart from hurting my back, I've been a very healthy person, I don't have ongoing pain in any way, so – but, my God, I did have a lot of emotional pain and that went on for a very long time – in fact I ended up having psychotherapy myself for four years when he had psychoanalysis. F7

Pain as positive

Pain was not, in general, necessarily viewed as entirely negative; it ranged from being seen as a sign of health, a warning to the body, as in acute, usually physical pain:

> I don't think pain is necessarily negative – it's the body telling you something, at least with acute pain. I mean, I'd be very upset if I didn't have any nerve endings. And, I mean, you do come across people who don't have that facility and it's very upsetting because they can't walk around, they have to walk around in a so-to-speak bubble. M2

> No, I think people grow from pain. Thinking of mental pain, I mean grief – that can make you – it's not nice to feel it, obviously – but it can make you a stronger person, a more aware person, of the things that are going on around you. Like watching whales being slaughtered – that isn't a nice thing to see but if people don't see it then they won't believe they do feel pain and they won't do anything about it so I think pain can be . . . it depends what sort, like physical pain – if you touch something hot, then yes, that teaches you not to do it again but if you get pain like rheumatism, that sort of long-lasting, nothing-you-can-do-about pain, that isn't good – no one can learn anything from that. So sort of short-term it is useful, it can teach you – it is healthy to feel pain because it means you've got all your senses in working order so you don't damage yourself. F6

Pain can even be described as 'productive'. This was often the case with childbirth, at least when it resulted in a live birth. In fact, only one of the women in the sub-sample had rated childbirth as her most painful experience (Suni F3). However, Suni had already given birth to two other children, but her third labour had resulted in a lengthy Caesarean, and she felt that the increased pain was associated with everything going 'wrong'. Elaine explains why she considered an ear abscess to be far more painful than any of her four labours:

> I think that any woman who's had a baby isn't going to exaggerate – you've got a much better understanding, I think, of whether things really do hurt or not. So I had this abscess and I thought that was much worse than labour because that was sort of sheer undiluted pain whereas in labour the pain is sort of mixed in with all sorts of other feelings – I think that the feeling of this other person inside you wanting to get out is stronger than just sheer sort of pain that makes

you want to bang your head against a brick wall, which is what I
thought the abscess was like and I couldn't eat or sleep or talk, I
couldn't get away from it at all and I'm not very good at bearing that
kind of pain, I suppose because I thought there's no point to it either.
Where with childbirth – I'm not one of these people who says it
doesn't hurt, maybe for some people it doesn't but it does for me . . .
but it's different, it's not sort of pointless pain that sends you out of
your mind, partly because it comes in waves anyway and it's only for
a short time altogether and then I think this sort of feeling of the
baby trying to get out is stronger . . . I've had the fourth baby now
and I haven't changed my mind. F4

Losing control

The issue of control is central; locus of control is a much-tested
psychological variable in experimental research. Pain becomes increasingly
negative the more uncontrollable it becomes. It is also more likely to be
viewed negatively when chronic and/or terminal:

> Pain is only negative if it doesn't go away – it's positive in that it
> alerts you that something's wrong, you have to take things easier or
> whatever . . . but it's when it's caused by some insidious disease you
> can't cure – then it's a *real* pain! M6

When the pain is unable to be controlled, it appears to be more threatening:

> I don't know because I think it goes hand in hand with the mental
> frustration as well, depending on where it is – with the toothache I
> think I got to the point where I was in a state of panic, that feeling of
> desperation because it was so persistent, mentally it's a larger ordeal
> than just the toothache itself. Also the more it didn't get sorted out –
> I just got to the stage where I wanted to say to pull out the tooth,
> that was the only way I could see any release. M4

> It depends, when you're angry and you hit someone or hit something
> to get rid of your anger then you don't initially feel the pain, it's only
> afterwards when you're more relaxed and calm you feel what you've
> actually done. Because I know that once, a long time ago I had a
> complete temper tantrum and I just stormed out of the house and out
> into the back garden and bashed my hand against the wall and I
> didn't actually feel it till I came in and it was all grazed and bloody
> and then it started to hurt – but at the time I think my emotion of

anger overcame the pain, so it's – also when you're upset pain is more painful – when you're like tearful anyway or sort of depressed – it's a lot to do with attitude – if you're in a very good mood and you hurt yourself you tend to laugh it off. F6

The location of pain in the body may be important. Helena (F5) felt that the emotional pain of the removal of her ovaries, and the subsequent implications of childlessness, exacerbated and were worse to bear than any physical suffering she had endured. Tim (M4) described how humiliated he felt by the removal of varicose veins from his testicles, a few weeks before his wedding, which again far outweighed the physical hurt. Pain in the region of the head was thought to be particularly hard to endure:

> I think if you've got a bad foot or if you've got a pain in wherever else in your body it's still possible to go about your daily business if you have to. But if you've got a headache or migraine or something like that it tends to throw you so completely you're not able to cope with everyday things because it's like a battering. M11

> I think some parts of your body are more amenable to that so you can put up with them more whereas pain anywhere to do with your head is impossible to get away from. Apart from taking strong painkillers, which I don't think even work, you can't make it better. M2

Chronic and/or terminal pain is linked with depression, poor self-esteem and mental illness. Again, the issue of control is central here, and can be linked to a sense of powerlessness. Explanations sought for such pain often involve self-blame. For instance, Peter repeatedly mentioned that he thought he had neglected his health in the past and felt that it was seen to be an important factor in the development of his malignant tumours, especially by health professionals:

> One thing that worried me about the Bristol approach [to cancer] was that deliberately or accidentally it seemed to encourage the attitude that patients were in some way responsible for their illness, that they had brought it upon themselves. I've been thinking about that a lot and I do acknowledge that in the past I have neglected my own health and been casual about it but to say that I had wanted in some strange way to be ill seems iffy. I think there are many factors involved. There is the economic factor – I've been unemployed on and off for a long time. There's the question of ignorance – having come from a privileged background where I never had to cook I'm bad at cooking for myself . . . there are enough problems in coping with the pain without worrying about the stigma. M10

Helen had a strong sense of self-blame and failure, which she expressed in almost punitive terms, resulting from the disabilities incurred
from a hit-and-run accident:

> Before my accident I was a carefree, very with-it, I could always . . .
> sort of think what the day was and what I was going to do this time
> next week, on Tuesday I must get my order ready for my groceries
> and what-not. Now, I don't know from one day to the other what the
> day is and what I've got to do – I look, think 'oh it's 2 o'clock and I've
> made no lunch' and things like that – I've lost all my preciseness – it's
> all gone by the board, I'm just an old, an old has-been now, I feel. F2

Pain as punishment

Other respondents who had experienced traumatic events in their
lives expressed beliefs about experiences of pain as a form of punishment.
Marie (F9) felt that the burden of caring for her husband with Alzheimer's
disease, in nightmare conditions, was ordained by God and used her Catholic
faith both to explain and sustain her predicament. Sean (M1), on the other
hand, had developed a complex belief system around religion and race to
explain his misfortunes. He was aware that his views were subject to much
disapproval within his circle of family and friends. Nevertheless he felt
very strongly that all his problems, both medical and emotional, and the
resultant pain he had to endure, resulted from his being what he termed
'a cross-breed' (see case study, pp. 104–6)

> I don't mean in terms of colour but I'm meant to be Irish but I'm not
> really pure . . . it's all to do with the Jews. My mum's real mother died
> when my mum was only 17, she was Jewish . . . I think it's a curse
> that follows people around and now I think it's following me and I
> blame a lot of the problems that I have . . . M1

Treatment by health professionals was a major issue (see the case study
of Rachel's story, p. 102). A crucial factor, expressed by all the respondents,
in the ability to stay in control and subsequently cope with pain was the
amount of knowledge and information about what was happening to them.
Patrick (M11) broke down and cried as he described how he was told
of his HIV-positive status; he felt that the doctor had such contempt
for him that he was unable to ask for any information or support. Peter
(M10) related how humiliated he felt when an examining doctor com-
mented on his low pain threshold due to Peter's flinching away from an
unexpectedly painful probe.

Conclusion

The location and nature of these interviews as a context for the expression of experiences and beliefs about pain differed from those of the questionnaire survey. The interviews took place outside the clinical environment of the GP's surgery, and were more intimate and informal than the questionnaire completion. These differences may account in part for the intensely personal accounts of pain that emerged.

Several contradictory themes emerged from the data analysis. On the one hand, conceptualisations of pain appear to transcend the dualistic mechanistic assumptions inherent in Western biomedicine and pain is seen to have emotional and existential, as well as physical, aspects. On the other hand, there appears to be a belief that there are *hierarchies* of pain, in the sense that some forms of pain are more socially acceptable than others. Obviously this may vary by social group or by culture, and it is not possible to make sweeping generalisations from a sample of this size, but despite the trend towards holistic conceptualisation, pain with a patholo-gical, usually physical, cause appears to have more respectability, validity and authenticity and is more of an issue for men than for women. The women in the sample were more likely to acknowledge their emotional vulnerability, and to emphasise its impact on their ability to feel pain or not. Philosophical threads of 'pain as growth' examined in earlier chapters are borne out by these accounts. Certainly the Hippocratic assumption that pain always needs to be alleviated or relieved was refuted by many of the respondents with the theme that there are both positive and negative aspects of pain. If pain is acute, it can be seen as a sign of health, both physically and emotionally, in the sense of providing a signal function to both mind and body. Pain can even be seen as productive, as in childbirth. How-ever, if the cause of the pain is indeterminable and it becomes chronic, the person loses control, which is seen as a crucial negative component. Increasingly, explanations and mechanisms to help to 'cope' become attached to the external world, and may incorporate existential beliefs. These may be spiritual, even religious, or may be a search for rationality. Many of the respondents cited the need for knowledge and information to pro-vide reassurance and sustainment. The attainment of these qualities can be shown to be dependent on a person's status in the social structure. It follows that inequalities in status such as gender, race or class may act to marginalise access to such strategies.

Case studies

Tim's story, case study M4

Aged 25, Tim thought that he was English, but was unable to say for sure as he had never known his parents, spending a large part of his childhood in children's homes. He wanted to be a theatre designer, and, despite leaving school at 16, had obtained an honours degree in the subject. He was currently unemployed, but finding occasional acting parts. Having very recently married, he lived in a squat with his wife and an artist friend; the interview took place squeezed among many canvases. Tim had experienced a variety of health problems over the last year, including a hernia, frequent bouts of influenza, and a varicose vein on a testicle needing removal. When responding to the questionnaire, Tim described his worst pain experience as a toothache, which persisted over a whole weekend, as he was unable to get emergency treatment. He felt the pain to be so acute that he lost control and punched his fist into a picture frame, gashing his hand severely.

Tim had also mentioned in the questionnaire that he had been suffering from what he described as 'panic attacks'. By the time of the interview, these had become much worse and had an extremely debilitating effect upon his life, as the following account shows:

> I have been experiencing what has been described as panic attacks but
> I don't know if it's a really suitable description, the first time it was
> like a depersonalisation and once that occurred, for the next four or
> five days, whatever I did, when I picked up a cup or looked in the
> mirror, I felt totally separate from whatever was going on – it was like
> an inner terror . . . it's gone and it's come back and I've been seeing
> a psychologist for seven months and I'm going to have acupuncture.
> It always comes at completely illogical times, it's not as if I'm a
> depressive – I don't have a recurrent theme in my head. It can come
> when I'm feeling incredibly happy and relaxed, that's what's so
> frustrating about it . . . because the whole time I've been convinced
> it's something physical, obviously, because it makes it that much
> easier to bear, and more respectable somehow – I mean, I still think
> maybe I've got a chemical imbalance or I ought to try maybe more
> homeopathic things, I don't know that much about it but it just
> seems like sitting in a room with some bloke talking about my
> childhood doesn't bear any kind of relation to the kind of feelings I'm
> going through. And I mean it is like a physical pain at times, it's like

a vice on my temples and an incredible pressure on my head that it does produce a headache but essentially it's just a brooding feeling within the skull. That's why, I mean, I've been to see doctors and GPs and I really wanted to have a brain scan and all these things. The longer it's gone on the more I've sort of come to terms with it – I always carry diazepam, it's like a safety measure – I very rarely use it but it's nice to know it's there.

He was very insistent that he would have preferred his distress to have a physical cause, which he would have felt to be more 'respectable' than the presumably psychological nature of the condition and was very unhappy about the treatment on offer, namely psychotherapy, which he did not feel helped him with the 'here-and-now'. Tim said he found the interview helpful, and he had found some relief in being able to discuss his experiences. He enjoyed the imagery sequence especially, as he could use his artistic knowledge, which helped his self-esteem.

Peter's story, case study M10

Peter, aged 53, was an ex-journalist who had left his native South Africa in the late 1960s as a 'white' protest against the apartheid regime. He had been used to an affluent, privileged lifestyle which became progressively downwardly mobile in exile, exacerbated by bouts of depression, and leading to a difficult divorce and the loss of his job. Five years before the interview, he developed the first of three cancer 'attacks': carcinomas were found in his left arm, buttock and leg, which resulted in a number of operations, including the amputation of his left leg. He did attend a pain clinic, but did not find it helpful, and relied on regular analgesia to manage the pain. He attributes his pain to be the result of amputation, rather than 'cancer pain':

> I don't think of what I'm suffering as cancer pain though, I think of it entirely as pain resulting from the operations. I don't even acknowledge that there is such a thing as cancer pain – I just think there's pain and that the pain – it wasn't pain exactly in the same way – there was a feeling of illness and physical debilitation and breakdown before I went to the medics but that was quite different from the sharp *physical* pain that I have felt which I feel is due to the severing of the nerves in the operation which is how I crudely understand it . . .

but which can dissipate if he becomes distracted and especially if intellectually stimulated (he claimed to enjoy the interview so much that he forgot to take his prescription, and did not notice the pain until the interview finished).

Peter lived on his own in a basement flat owned by a housing co-operative, and spent most of his time in the living room which was stacked with waist-high piles of newspapers and books, to which he repeatedly referred for reference during the interview. He was extremely agile on his crutches, and apart from accepting Invalidity Benefit and Meals-on-Wheels, he completely resisted adopting 'sick-role' behaviour. His daily life involved a constant stream of visitors and friends, who, he maintains, use his flat as a meeting-place to discuss politics, literature, the arts or indeed any desired topic. At various points in the interview, he requested that the tape-recorder be turned off, so that he could 'chat', which included asking me about my own life, to which I acquiesced. Despite all that he had suffered, he was intensely optimistic, also witty and amusing, and at times I felt unsure who was interviewing whom.

Peter had spent a lot of time contemplating and working out his own philosophical stance on pain; for instance, he thought that 'physical pain can be a means of solving your emotional problems – it drowns out depression or whatever because it's so immediate and intense'. He felt that his bouts of depression, which he termed 'the black dog', were much more painful than anything he had coped with physically, especially as he felt it to be responsible for his wife's leaving him. Although he did not want to convey the impression that he had wanted to become ill in any way, for Peter, pain had a spiritual component (not in a religious sense), but having cancer had taught him the beauty of life and he believed the quality of his life to be higher than ever before. He derived tremendous pleasure from the imagery sequence, and expressed the view that this kind of research should take place in pain clinics, as not only would it inform the researcher but it would be of great therapeutic value to the researched.

Rachel's story, case study F10

Aged 34 and 'white British', Rachel had trained as a general nurse and midwife, then took a higher degree in community health and was working full-time as an immunisation facilitator at the time of the interview. When she completed the questionnaire in the GP surgery, her most painful experience had been due to an incident in hospital where she had been neglected in the middle of wound treatment; the dressing for a skin graft on her leg was being changed and the wound was left exposed for half an hour. She had already experienced many painful incidents with the leg since she injured it in a motorcycle incident in Bangladesh two years previously. As well as the trauma of travelling back to England with a smashed leg, she had undergone extensive treatment and plastic surgery, but felt that this incident was made worse by the neglect and humiliating treatment of the nursing and medical staff:

> It's definitely more complicated than just a physical sensation – in my experience the whole thing of having my leg smashed up and surgery five or six times, being in intensive care and all that – the times when I was getting information about what was happening, the times when I wasn't afraid I was being kept in the dark about it, the times when I felt supported, were the times when you know I could deal with the pain much better and it was the times when I didn't feel like I had that support and I didn't feel that people were honest with me that I found it much harder to handle.

In the six months that had elapsed between our encounter in the surgery and the interview, she felt that her life had changed dramatically – her hospital experiences prompted the change of direction in her career. Pain was something that she had thought about a great deal and had changed her own conceptualisation, thinking that she had always defined it in narrower sensory terms. This was further exacerbated by the decision of her partner to leave her, three months previous to the interview, and she felt that the emotional pain that she had to endure as a consequence was far worse than any physical pain she had experienced:

> I think you can see *physical* pain as a result of *emotional* trauma . . . like you asked how you see things in your life affecting your health and one thing I put was things going well within the primary relationship and – I've recently split up from my partner in the last few weeks and I know that some of the *emotional* pain I've had from that has been experienced *physically* in terms of, um, really aching inside all around the stomach and – I'm sure that's an *emotional* thing but I can feel it *physically* . . . I think that – it may be different for different people but I know that *emotional* pain and stress manifest themselves in *physical* ways in me and I can recognise my stress responses and I do get sort of aching inside and I come out in cold sores. On one occasion I came out in an incredible itchy rash and as soon as you start dealing with the stress that's provoking that, then it stops. There's probably something in between that, it's a two-step thing . . . but the *emotional* pain goes on longer – I think it's somehow worse than a *physical* pain because that is usually comprehensible, logical and there's a certain amount of control – you can get your head round it but I'd rather go through half an hour of what I

described happened to me in hospital than two months of what I've just been through.

She claimed to find both the interview and the imagery sequence helpful, but was disturbed by some of the images and found them very distasteful.

Sean's story, case study M1

Aged 28, Sean works full-time as a double-glazing salesman. He left school aged 16 and has no formal school-leaving qualifications. He lives with his parents, who own their own home, and describes his nationality as Irish, as well as describing his ethnic (and religious) background in great detail on the questionnaire thus: father Irish Catholic, mother English Catholic, maternal grandmother English Jewish. This background held much significance for Sean, especially with regard to his health:

> I can only stress that my problems have been caused because I am a cross-breed. I am in no way racialist or prejudiced and I do not mean any offence to anyone. I blame my problems on the fact that I am not of one nationality and I feel all people should be – my views are directed at a person's blood and not at the colour of their skin. I am white skinned but I feel all men and women – black, white, yellow – are good as long as they are full-breeds. I add I feel more mental pain than physical. I would help anyone if I could and I like to give the impression that I'm very happy when really I'm not.

For the last fifteen years, he had suffered from an endocrinal disorder which he does not know the name of, and finds embarrassing to discuss, involving a hormone deficiency requiring regular injections. He described the humiliation that this caused him as an adolescent, as many of the normal pubescent changes did not occur, such as his voice breaking. He did not seek or receive treatment for the condition until the age of 21, which Sean claims only happened because his elder sister insisted that something should be done, as her boyfriend was incessantly teasing him. Until this time Sean maintains that he just ignored the condition, but reflects that it has always made him feel 'odd' and marginalised, and he was often called a 'poof'.

In the questionnaire, Sean had described the most painful experience he could remember, which involved being beaten with a belt by his father for wetting the bed when he was aged about 9.

> Like if you're a kid and you have an accident, the sympathy is there afterwards, like with stitches in your head and people giving you

sweets, you're sort of like a celebrity at school, it's like being famous. Although the pain part of it wasn't very nice, afterwards was good. But what came after wetting the bed, it's just more – you've done it again, the humiliation, not just being beaten . . . My dad, he never gave much to me. He didn't give us a hiding just for no reason but, not like some people do, but for wetting the bed, anything like that he used to give it with a strap and get my face rubbed in it, all that – well, that would be the worst thing, you know, and not having things other kids have – even now I'm very bitter about it but I don't show it, you know, to other people. I get very depressed, not just about that but for other reasons, other people don't know because I don't show it, I hide it but it's there all the time.

This had happened recurrently throughout his childhood and he expressed a great deal of bitterness and resentment against his father throughout the interview but ascribed many of his father's 'faults' to the evils of intermarriage. As the interview progressed, it became clear that he had built up an extremely complex belief system around this condition involving his ethnic background. He saw it as manifesting as a constant 'mental pain' which, in his view, was much worse than any physical suffering he could imagine and felt that life had treated him very unfairly:

I feel that all the pain I've suffered comes back to the fact that basically I'm a cross-breed, I don't mean in terms of colour but I'm meant to be Irish but I'm not really, not pure . . . I suppose I'm the only one in the family that feels that – I've said it to them, I've even said to my mum – she didn't like it but she's had a lot of problems and I said to her one day that it's all to do with the Jews. My mum's real mother died when my mum was only 17, she was Jewish – the grandad's been married twice since, he's still alive and in good health but she died of cancer and I said to my mum one day, the reason you're having problems with your legs and your knees now is because of the Jews, because of the curse upon them – because going back to religion again, because they crucified Christ. But it I said that to a Jewish person they'd take offence and I don't mean to offend them, I'm not anti-Jewish but I think a Jew should be a Jew and a Catholic – well, that's just religion . . . but people should be what they are, there's no sense of identity any more, like patriotism is a dirty word. I think people should be given back a sense of identity as something to even fight for if it came to it but there's nothing . . . at times it really bothers me, at others it don't. When I say to people, I blame the Jews I don't mean to, er . . . I think it's a curse that follows people around and now I think it's following me and I blame a lot of the problems that I have – but you've got to be careful what you say to people and sometimes you bottle things up rather than say it.

Despite the fact that Sean perceived himself as unlucky and something of a misfit, he gave a very lively, animated interview, peppered with jokes, some of which I privately found offensive due to their sexist/racist flavour. Sean was able to express highly complex and abstract belief patterns incorporating social characteristics such as race and class, as well as existential notions of fate and destiny. He enjoyed using the imagery very much and gave very detailed imaginative responses, incorporating comparisons with popular films and TV programmes.

chapter 6

'All men do is shave': gendered beliefs about pain

The theoretical framework of this study infers that biological differences and factors such as sex roles, the cultural socialisation of males and females and stereotyped assumptions of health practitioners may all constitute possible explanations of gender differences in health and illness and that this approach may be applied to understand possible differences in perceptions of pain. One of the main research questions examined the relationship between gender roles and perceptions of pain, and in particular whether there are cultural assumptions about the ability of women and men to 'cope' with pain. The questionnaire findings supported the view expressed in many attitude surveys, namely that women were thought to be more able to cope with pain, as in the young man who reckoned that pain was something that women were attuned to in their everyday lives from puberty onwards whereas 'all we do is shave'. This finding is discrepant with much of the psychophysical experimental research, which tends to favour women's pain thresholds being *lower* than men's. Open-ended material collected in the questionnaire asked respondents to articulate the reasoning behind their views on gender and pain; analysis of these data revealed a variety of reasons and beliefs, many of which were extremely complex explanations that were conceptually sophisticated and transcended the dualisms perpetrated by reductionist scientific divides of mind and body, nature and nurture. It was hypothesised that the potential flexibility and subjective nature of the interview would act to cultivate further contemplation. The aim of this chapter, therefore, is to draw on the interview material in attempting to 'tease out' gendered notions of pain.

Questionnaires versus interviews

After respondents had talked in detail about their most painful experiences (which, in turn, opened up discussions about the nature of pain), and had considered the visual imagery, they were reminded of the questionnaire, and asked if they could remember what they had said in answer to the question as to whether they thought there were any differences in the abilities of men and women to cope with pain. Of the twenty men and women who fully completed the interview (two respondents began the interview but did not complete it), nine remembered their answers accurately. Seven respondents (two women and five men) changed their opinion completely from the questionnaires to the interviews. These changes were all from the 'no differences' or 'don't know' category to 'women cope better'. There could be various reasons for the changed responses. One obvious explanation is the time interval between completing the questionnaires and the interviews (six months), which allowed for genuine changes of mind. Another possibility is the effect of my, the interviewer's, gender although, as I also handed out all the questionnaires, it does not seem likely that this is the explanation. Indeed, other research findings go against this interpretation, in suggesting that, in the presence of women, men are more likely to say that men cope better. In an experiment conducted to investigate the effect of experimenter gender on the pain reports of male and female subjects, respondents (thirty-three female and thirty-five male North American psychology undergraduates aged 17–29) were asked to rate cold pressor pain[1] in front of either male or female experimenters. The results indicated that males reported significantly less pain in front of a female experimenter than a male, whereas the difference in female subjects was not significant, although they tended to report higher pain to the male experimenters. The authors conclude:

> The result is congruent with the standard gender role requirement of males appearing macho and not allowing females to know they are weak. The overall implications of this experiment are that pain report between the genders is not a simple difference of pain sensitivity. Rather it appears to be under the *social influence* of the gender of the person to whom the report is made.
>
> (Levine and de Simone 1991: 71)

---

1. The cold pressor test is conducted by subjects placing their hands up to the wrists in a hard rubber bucket filled with ice-water and a layer of floating ice cubes at a temperature of 0–1°C and rating the subsequent pain on scales measuring both sensory and affective scales.

It is interesting to speculate whether the change of opinion that took place in the interviews would have been the same had the interviewer been male.

Other studies (see, for example, Oakley, Rajan and Robertson 1990) have noted the tendency for questionnaires and interviews to yield different responses. For certain kinds of data, it would seem that the more anonymous context of a questionnaire encourages the confiding of sensitive information. Although none of the men who changed their minds in this study could remember what they had originally indicated on the questionnaire, both women did remember. They claimed that their opinion had changed in the intervening time, due to personal experiences.

Why do women cope better?

Nobody in the interview sample expressed the view that men were more able to cope with pain, and only one man, Bob (M9), maintained the view that there are no differences. His rationale was as follows:

> But overall, about the same – that definitely one way or the other
> as regards physical pain – I mean, you've both got the same central
> nervous systems – what's going to hurt someone whether they're male
> or female – the pain is going to be the same. If it's not psychological
> then I would say it would be the same.
> Q: What if it were psychological?
> Well, that would vary between individuals, some people are far more
> sensitive than others – they feel – some are a lot harder through
> experience than others so it's easier to block out psychological pain.
> Like at this stage now, very little would give me too much
> psychological pain, I would just block it out and not dwell on it
> whereas someone younger would get very upset over things now
> I wouldn't blink at. I think psychological pain is an individual thing
> whereas physical pain would be the same, male or female.

In spite of worries expressed over making generalisations, everyone else in the sample stressed the view that women were inherently more able to cope with pain. The relative informality of the interview provided an opportunity to examine in more depth why this opinion was so firmly held. Many of the men stressed that it was a popular *belief*, for example:

> It's difficult to say – one is brought up to think that women cope
> better with pain . . . I think they have a bigger threshold – whether
> that's a purely subjective view . . . M3

Oh, women are better at coping with pain.
Q: Why do you think that is?
It's, er, sort of folklore but I think it's true. M5

Well, that's the only reason I put it, it's a general belief – women
have to go through labour so . . . As far as I can gather it's just
something in the make-up of women that's different to men . . . but
whether it's something you can scientifically prove, I don't know . . .
It might be one of those myths – like strength. A man is supposed to
be stronger than a woman but women are stronger emotionally and
can stand more pain. M6

Especially the men in the sample portray childbirth as the ultimate
painful experience. For instance, Peter (M10), despite his personal experience over five years of malignant tumours resulting in amputations, still
maintained that the worst possible pain he could imagine would be childbirth. He felt that, in turn, women's ability to reproduce gave them a
'natural' advantage to cope with pain:

My hunch is that has to do with childbearing, I remember a sense of
awe and fear even when [his son] was born – I could hear [his wife]
shrieking and screaming from where I was in the hospital waiting
room. There was a sense that I would never know that extreme of
pain that she was undergoing.
Q: Would you say that now?
Yes I would, and I do think that many men do have that awe and the
sense that this is the ultimate pain, that there can be no worse and of
course we don't know and we can't know what childbearing is like.
And there are many different attitudes towards the pain but as far as
I can gather most women seem to feel it's worth it.

The view was repeatedly expressed by both women and men that
the combination of female biology and the reproductive role served to equip
girls and women with a 'natural' capacity to endure pain, not only physically but also emotionally. This 'natural' attribution of women re-evokes
the well-known distinction between public and private domains. Among
others, Martin (1987) points out that women are intrinsically linked with
the family, which is the location of bodily and 'lower' functions, whereas
men are more readily associated with cultural, mental and 'higher' processes of the public world of paid work. This theme recurred frequently
in connection with pain perceptions and beliefs, and was articulated by
all the respondents in some form:

I suppose one naturally expects women within the course of a healthy life to be involved with pain but not men on the whole – unless they get hit with hammers. M3

I wouldn't think it's a learnt thing, I think it is an actual biological difference. Although there might be women who are brought up to – well, be beaten all the time, they might get used to it, like battered wives or something. M6

I think partly because women are more in touch with their feelings and they have certain yardsticks, not just having babies but periods, things happening to their bodies that they aren't in control of so they think about their bodies more and they learn to live with discomfort, I suppose. Most people find periods uncomfortable if not painful, and the same about pregnancy – some women enjoy being pregnant but others find it mildly irritating and uncomfortable. Even things like breastfeeding – when do men ever experience anything like having cracked nipples but still carrying on with it – things like that. I think women just have more contact with their *natural biological part* [sic] and they are just more inclined to think about it and analyse it and not just complain about it which I think, well in my experience, is what men do, really. They're not really interested in the causes of pain or sort of in seeing themselves in relation to the pain, but they think of it as an outside irritant that's got to be dealt with. F4

As in the open-ended data generated by the questionnaire, the inter-view revealed sophisticated explanations ranging right across the biological and sociocultural frameworks described earlier. Although many explanations began with a biological basis, they led in to role expectations:

Women are made to suffer pain because we have periods and childbirth. Whatever happens, women end up bringing up children, we just don't have the 'privilege' of giving in to pain and sickness. F3

I think that women cope better or have to cope better, well, I think they have to because a man can go off to bed if he's feeling ill but a woman has still got the kids there or they're not really allowed to be ill – they don't think, she still has to get the jobs done – the kids are screaming for attention, they don't really understand that mum's not well 'cos if dad's not well he'd be in bed . . . so I'd have to say that possibly it's worse for a woman, physically and mentally probably because they're not allowed to show it. The man only has to provide the earnings, well, in a lot of cases the woman has to provide money too . . . so women suffer more – it's a man's world really in that respect. M1

I mean, people do say that women can take more pain and this does seem to make sense to me but I think it's probably that it's different sorts of pain and I'm a bit wary of generalising. I think men have more fear really, which is what enables one to take or not take pain really – I think it's when you're afraid to some extent that you come apart . . . in a spiritual sense women are stronger – women are much more spiritually orientated than men and I know there are many men who also are but for women it comes much more *naturally*. Also women can . . . well, in our society we've got so confused about gender roles but in simpler cultures the women are used to doing the serving and so if something happens to them the attitude is more – oh, I can't give to others rather than what's going to happen to me . . . F5

I think women are much more stoic. I think women have a very strong sense of responsibility. I suspect that's developed by society, that's what they're expected to be but also some of it is inborn and that the propensity is there because of the protection of children and the next generation. Human children take so long to grow up – you have to be responsible for them a long time – so women tend to put their pain on one side while they get on with being responsible so in fact the needs of other people override the need to experience your own pain – I think particularly emotional pain. Physical pain, too, I think an awful lot of women just get on with their lives and maybe men too, so I'm not sure if it does split by gender but certainly the responsibility for small children does but that isn't the whole story . . . when you come to emotional pain, I think practically everybody runs a mile and I think women are better at expressing and acknowledging emotional pain than men are. Now ask that question again in fifty years because, say, twenty years ago, 99 per cent would never have admitted to emotional pain anyway – that's something that the women's movement, women's liberation – that's what women have been liberated from in many ways – this need to cover up and pretend everything is all right – they somehow find it possible to express and acknowledge their pain. But men are much worse at it – maybe they're more frightened – but it will probably come because I think there's a movement throughout society, more credence to the individual – there are different balances of home, leisure and work. F7

The conditioned stoicism of men

The theme of gender socialisation was also interwoven throughout the explanations. In contrast to the 'natural' biological capabilities of coping with pain attributed to women, it was felt that childhood socialisation actively discouraged emotional expression in boys, and adult males felt an obligation to display stoicism. Subsequently, the experiences of many men and women are that, for men, pain of any sort is abnormal and outside their expectations, and they are consequently less able to deal with it (see case studies of Janina, p. 120, and James, p. 121). The phenomenon of 'macho' conditioning was a recurrent theme for many of the respondents:

> I think a woman would be more likely to seek help than a man would because I don't think a man would accept that there's anything wrong with them. Women would be the more sensible and the men would be more stubborn – it's a form of brainwashing, it's just – like at school you see a boy in the corner crying for his mum, but a girl it wasn't the same – the boy is a sissy or whatever, with the girl it's a form of brainwashing, you don't even realise it, like – boys it's all action men and guns and you know, they're taught to be tough where girls have all little dolls and things to dress up. Apart from the odd exception, the majority – it's done without even realising, it's a form of brainwashing, television and everything, you know, maybe it shouldn't be you know but that's the way it is, you're not allowed to show your feelings, you're not meant to but why shouldn't you? It's just not accepted. There are different cases but that's a general view of the way it is. M1

> I think women of a certain age are ready to consider the pain of childbirth – they know about it. Maybe a 4-year-old seeing a woman on TV biting and screaming doesn't know what's going on, but by age 8 they see, they learn, they hear and gradually the psychological resistance builds up – I believe in the power of the mind and that it affects the physiological threshold. I don't know if that's very clear but I think that men are – historically they've been in a position of strength – muscular power, all that sort of thing. All they've got to do with children is to mind them a couple of days a week but, um, feel vulnerable when in pain and therefore that vulnerability can be exacerbated by the fact that they are feeling pain, feeling 'why should I feel that – why me when I'm so strong, I am a man' and the doubt and vulnerability goes on for a while. Conversely you could get

someone who doesn't feel that at all . . . I was thinking about the
reactions of a girl child and a boy child to blood, as a result of a cut
and I would generally imagine that the girl it would be 'Oh, I'm
bleeding' but the macho act of the young boy would be 'I've got a cut
but I'm all right – I've got a plaster, look at my scar'. Not that I don't
think that girls could act like that but the conditioning of boys to be
macho is very strong . . . M8

There is a recurrent theme of women's emotional 'day-to-day'
resilience, acting as a socialised form of 'buffering', whereas men, as in
Beecher's famous wounded soldiers, are seen as being more capable of heroic
pain through war or sport. Without this heroic aspect, on an everyday level
men's capacities are treated with some derision:

In your childhood you're not brought up in a vacuum, like you see in
problem pages in women's magazines, letters from mothers – 'I'm
worried about my son, he's timid, he likes cooking and things – is he
gay?' In other words, you're only allowed to be sincere and sensitive
if you admit to being gay, being like a woman. In this society, even
men who are aware of it and don't like it, have to obey the rules – it's
so drilled into you from childhood, you just can't escape it – to admit
to being as sensitive as a woman, it's very difficult to overcome those
social barriers. The more artistic – artists are allowed to be expressive,
sensitive, whereas scientific people have to be rational and sensible
all the time. It is odd to see a man cry. I don't think there's
anything bad about it, it's just that it's so rare. Maybe if a woman was
brought up in the same way – you mustn't cry, go and play football
instead . . . women themselves, even the most feministic, still go sort
of helpless – oh please – sidle up and get what they want – I'm sure
that happens to the best of us. F6

Both men and women in this sample perceive the negative effects
of this conditioning:

When I was working as a midwife we always reckoned that if it was
men who had the babies the birth-rate would drop in negative
proportions!
Q: So why do you think women do cope better?
Well, we're brought up that way – a lot of that is nature/nurture sort
of stuff but at the same time we're brought up to be allowed to
express it – big boys don't cry and all that sort of thing whereas girls
are allowed to cry, they are allowed to express their pain – it's
probably just as well because I think women do go through much
more pain – emotionally – they're more likely to address it and deal

with it rather than – men are more likely to repress it and it comes
out in aggression . . .

Q: What do you mean by the nature/nurture stuff?

Well, it starts at day 1 really . . . there are very clear differences in the
way that boys and girls behave and develop but what is often
superimposed upon that is what is acceptable and what isn't
acceptable. I've never had a child so I don't have first-hand experience
but the children I've been around – the damage that parents can do
to kids, telling them that they cannot, will not behave in a certain
way – it's enormous. Well, it's partly parents and partly peer pressure
but I really don't know – I think they definitely develop differently.
Yet you see men, when faced with severe pain, go totally to pieces in
a way that women don't, usually. But it seems that women are much
more stoical about things like dysmenorrhoea than a man would be
experiencing the same kind of pain. F10

Well, because women are more down-to-earth individuals and grin
and bear it – if they have something wrong with them they either try
to get the doctor to sort it out for them or they try to snap out of it
themselves. F2

Expressing pain: benefits and costs

In attempting to make generalisations, the patterning of pain coping
by gender can be seen as ambiguous and ambivalent:

Women are more prone to depressions, they're more prone to things
sort of swamping over them, they indulge in it, stay at home all day
and eat – um, let me think, well, men get looked after by their
women-folk. Women have to sort of strive and get on with it,
whatever, whereas men can indulge themselves more. Women are
actually stronger, they don't have illnesses so much . . . When you
think of individuals, I've got an aunt who whinges about the slightest
pain, she's in pain all the time. It sort of goes this way and that. You
get the sense of thinking that men will try and battle it out and don't
take a painkiller at the first sign whereas women will. On the flip side
of that, women are more practical, they won't accept pain – it goes
this way and that. If a woman's got pain and lots of kids she has to
hang on and look after them. As a boy I was always told that the
good Indian suffers in quiet. M2

The perceived superiority of capacities of endurance is double-edged
for women – the assumption that they may be able to 'cope' better may

lead to the expectation that they can put up with more pain, that their pain does not need to be taken so seriously:

> It's easier to be a man but maybe that's because I am a man and that's the way I've been led to think. I can only see it personally like the world according to – sort of thing. I do think the one thing with pain, when it's your mum or whatever you do find yourself thinking she can cope with it. The impression that I get is that women aren't supposed to feel pain. Now I would but as a kid I never felt any sympathy whatsoever, I didn't really understand . . . M1

> I think from my experience both being a nurse and a patient, doctors are much more likely to tell men what's going on, what's involved, especially when it's something surgical when it may be related to the workings of the combustion engine whereas they will assume that women are ignorant about the functioning of their body. Also often they don't relate very well to women, if you've got male/female, lay person/doctor and very often a class difference as well, and really being able to communicate with a female patient who maybe hasn't had a lot of education they find very difficult and they assume a lack of education much more. The trouble is that women doctors do the same . . . at one point I asked the consultant orthopaedic surgeon, when the bone in the leg wasn't healing and I asked him what sort of approaches he was going to take, like was he going to do a bone graft, was he going to do a plate – what was the range of possibilities. I wasn't asking him to decide then and there, I just wanted to know the range of possibilities I should be prepared for when I woke up and he turned round to me and said 'I'm not in the habit of discussing these things with patients' and I was furious. F10

> Well, I've never seen it in terms of being female but when I first developed the symptoms of what turned out later to be the brain tumour, for two years every doctor I went to told me I was depressed. And of course it's hard to know whether illness, pain, whatever, makes you depressed or if it's the other way round. And of course there were other things going on in my life which made me – if not clinically depressed, well, certainly down, like problems with my career, breaking up with a boyfriend, you know, things like that affect everyone. But my mother always said she knew it couldn't be depression because I was doing things that wouldn't indicate that – like planting the garden, little things maybe but which were important. But if I hadn't persevered, and my mother backed me up it may never have been diagnosed . . . F1

Being taken seriously was not perceived as just a gender issue, and other respondents felt that the colour of their skin or being working class meant that they were either ignored or not given information (see Angela's case study, pp. 122–3).

I'm very working-class in my relationship to doctors – I'm beholden to them – I don't trust them and I do a lot of exploration of myself. God knows what would happen if I were really ill because I think the service we're retaining now in the NHS isn't good enough. Back in the 60's my husband's mother, one the first wave of black women from the West Indies – she complained of pain – she was ignored and ended up having cancer of the ovaries and she died . . . OK, everyone's got their own collection of horror tales but there are too many of them – from people I know and in my working life – to just dismiss it. I think accessibility to health care is becoming more and more dependent on money – if you've got the money you can 'buy off' the pain to the extent of the information you obtain and the quality of service you receive. F8

I think there's a big ethnocentric thing about pain as well. I know that people would say, and supposedly quite astute intellectuals that – it's not just a racist thing but that women in Victorian times were used to their offspring dying – that because infant mortality rates were high that it wasn't that painful and I hear the same arguments about the families in India – that women there would be used to it and I think that's absolute shit because it demeans the whole relationship of one human being to another. M8

The notion that ageing implies an increased expectation of having to endure physical pain through illness was also strongly held. The implication is that the lower down in the social hierarchy the person is, the more likely they are to experience discrimination with pain, as in other areas of health and illness:

Yes, women cope better with pain but should they have to? The 'we're here to suffer' type thing . . . The collection of women I've seen suffering in my lifetime is enormous – maybe my eyes are attuned to women – much more enormous than the pain I've seen men suffer. I've seen women, black women particularly, and white women too, in enormous amounts of pain and just living with it. F8

Conclusion

Perceptions of pain-coping abilities are strongly gendered. In the interviews women are seen to have superior pain-coping capacities, and this
is explained in highly sophisticated terms underpinned with biological
principles, but embracing sociocultural themes of roles and socialisation.
Female hormonal and reproductive functioning and the role of motherhood
were consistently felt to equip girls and women with a 'natural' capacity
to endure pain, whereas for men pain was conceived of as 'abnormal'
and outside their 'natural' expectations and experience. The assumption of
women's superior pain-coping capacity may be double-edged, in that the
expectation of being able to cope can lead women to ignore pain. Similar
notions are, however, expressed in terms of race, class and age, and would
seem therefore to be a function of social minority group status. This would
suggest that to be disadvantaged in the wider social structure has implications for any understanding of the perception of pain.

Summary of findings

The findings of the study both reflect the particular experiences of
people living in a multi-racial inner-city area and provide a basis for developing new approaches to the understanding of pain, and the relationships
between pain, gender, culture and embodiment.
The main findings are summarised as follows:

1. Most people perceived that women have a superior capacity to
    men for coping with pain, or that there are no gender differences:
    a minority said that men were better at coping with pain.

2. In explaining these differences, interviewees identified female
    hormonal and reproductive functioning and the role of
    motherhood as equipping girls and women with a 'natural'
    capacity to endure pain, whereas no such biological preparation
    was identified for boys and men. Conversely, male socialisation
    was seen actively to discourage males from being allowed to
    express pain, whether physical or emotional. Expressing pain was
    thus considered a state of 'abnormality' for males, in contrast to
    the 'natural' attribution for females.

3. Analysis of the interview data, which incorporated responses
    to visual imagery, revealed that the meanings and definitions of

pain for the individual (both women *and* men) are not confined to physical sensations, but do include feelings and emotions, and spiritual and existential notions.

4. These broader meanings were notably more difficult to access using the instrument of a structured questionnaire as distinct from that of a semi-structured in-depth interview.

5. Analysis of the questionnaire data showed that men were less inclined to think that the emotional component of pain perception had any importance. However, in the interviews the male sub-sample discussed their feelings and vulnerabilities as freely as the women did. All the interview respondents acknowledged the concept of 'emotional' pain, but men were more likely to separate out these definitions and ascribe a hierarchy of 'respectability' to types of pain, whereas women gave more holistic, integrated accounts of their experiences.

These findings can be analysed on different levels. In Chapter 7 the methodological, theoretical and policy implications of the whole study are considered in turn. Finally, the contribution of the research to work in the area is discussed, along with directions of possible future research.

Case studies

Janina's story, case study F6

Janina is aged 18, and is in the sixth form at school, studying for
'A' levels. She describes herself as a British Jew with Polish maternal
grandparents, and lives with her mother, younger sister and stepfather in
a cramped but welcoming flat rented through a housing cooperative. The
interview took place in the kitchen, and the other household members
constantly and apologetically asked to come in and were very interested
in the research. Janina had some initial reservations about the interview
because she felt that she did not have much experience of pain, and repeated
what she had said in the questionnaire, that her worst memory was of
scalding her hand with a kettle when she was eight years old. She felt that
this had the effect of making her more afraid of hot things than she should
be, and she felt that fear had a lot to do with pain, although she considered that she had a high threshold, due to being very fit and healthy. As
the interview developed, Janina thought that from her experience, which
she considered limited due to her age, being emotionally hurt was much
more damaging than physical pain. With hindsight, she thought that some
of the fights she had with her sister were worse than the scalding incident. Her parents' marriage broke up when she was eleven, and she had a
very strong memory of her father being in a great deal of emotional pain
which he was unable to cope with or express in any way, whereas she felt
that her mother was able to 'cope' much better by asking for support and
being able to cry. Janina had grown up in a household with some experience of 'role reversal' in that her mother worked full-time, whereas her
step-father worked part-time and carried out most of the housework.
Although she did not see gender as necessarily 'fixed' or deterministic, she
strongly believed that there were important sociocultural differences:

> Men are not allowed socially to express pain as much, they're
> supposed to be stronger. We're allowed to cry and they're not . . .
> although women have more breakdowns than men, men don't allow
> it to come out, they hide it until it's unbearable whereas a woman
> will usually say 'I can't cope' long before. It's hard to avoid the
> indoctrination – you know men are stronger, therefore they could
> stand pain more but if I think about it logically I don't really think
> that . . . women can cope with mental pain a lot better. My parents
> are divorced and I know that my father still cannot cope with that,

with the pain associated with the divorce and the things around it whereas my mother has come to terms with it and is much more able to give. Obviously in her mind she has dealt with it and analysed it, done it to death really – worked it all out, why this happened and that happened. But as I said, it does depend on the person – I do have male friends who are extremely sensitive and very analytical. I'd say perhaps 40 per cent of my male friends are expressive and emotional whereas perhaps 90 per cent of my female friends are but you can't really say whether that's biological or society – in the social environment people think it's a sign of weakness to show pain but actually it's a sign of strength.

James's story, case study M3

Aged 38, James describes himself as white British and his occupation as an artist, although this does not supply an income and he works part-time as an interior decorator. His wife is a doctor. They own their own house, and agreed to experiment with role reversal when bringing up their two sons, now in their teens. (One of the sons, later admitting to curiosity as to what was happening, entered the dining room in the middle of the interview and proceeded to stub his toe, causing much merriment over this practical demonstration of pain!) James did not feel that he was much qualified to talk about pain, and had not had much experience of it – the worst thing that had happened to him personally was an infected varicose vein, which he did not feel counted for very much along a possible range. The most painful thing he had witnessed was his wife's labours, but felt that because there was a positive outcome, again this was not necessarily negative. He felt that the emotional response had as much validity as the physical, and that it might be more difficult to recover from wounds of the psyche. He thought the use of imagery was a valuable way to tap insights into pain beliefs, but could not stop himself responding 'technically' to the imagery, rather than emotionally.

James described a recent incident in which his youngest son, aged nine, had fallen over and cracked his skull. During the visit to Casualty, the boy wept continuously and profusely and was very upset. James expressed the view, rather apologetically, that he had felt his son to be making too much fuss, and expected him to be rather more stoical. He also admitted that he would not have had the same expectations of a girl, and also that he would not expect a female child to have such an accident in the first place.

Angela's story, case study F8

Angela, aged 36, arranged for me to interview her at her office. She works as a residential social worker in a psychiatric hostel. She claimed that it would be more difficult to talk at home, due to the lack of space in the privately rented three-bedroomed flat which is shared with her husband, her teenage daughter and her sister. Angela described herself as black British, her mother being Irish and her father having emigrated from Jamaica in the 1950s. When I initially contacted her, she was very keen to do the interview and emphasised how the questionnaire had helped her, as she completed it while waiting to see the doctor. At that time, she was seeing her GP with 'physical' complaints such as 'feeling run down', but found the subject matter of the study very pertinent to her own life. Angela experienced her life as extremely stressful and had been receiving psychotherapy for the last four years. In particular, she was still suffering from the bereavement of her mother, who had died the previous year, an event that Angela had indicated in the questionnaire as the most painful aspect of her life. I had talked to Angela several times on the telephone before the interview, as she had needed to rearrange the meeting, and had also sought reassurance about attending an outpatient appointment to investigate lumps in her breasts. When we finally did meet for the interview, Angela had obviously given the topics much thought, especially the psychological and emotional elements, and provided many profound and articulate insights. The themes were woven through both her working and personal life and she gave vivid and lucid responses to the imagery material.

> I'm guessing as it was a long time ago but I think the worst pain for me would be an emotional pain which for me is as valid as other types of pain – I always feel that physical pain somehow gets the attention – I'm not saying the two aren't related but for me I think the most painful experience if you qualify pain, emotional or physical, was when my mother died and I'm still not over that. Well, you see, I've not suffered physically that much – I don't even know if I'd say I'd suffered emotionally, I mean life is incredibly painful, it's perverse in a way. In my work if people come to me in pain there's something – there's something pure about pain, when people are going through pain it's instantly recognisable. And when you're going through it yourself, for me there's no ambiguity – I'm feeling pain. I'm sure it's got a certain power and currency but I wouldn't want to glamorise it because I think life and living should be as pain-free as possible because pain scars both emotionally and physically.

These themes were woven through her working life, as she was concerned with rehabilitation of the mentally ill and felt strongly that illness or disorders of a psychological or emotional nature were not given as much credibility as those with a demonstrable pathology. Although Angela was educated to higher degree level and was working as a qualified social worker, she regarded herself as 'working class' and felt that a person's class position was an important factor, as it would influence the amount of information and knowledge received and given. Similarly, Angela also felt that there were implications for the type of treatment given as regards ethnicity:

> Back in the 60s my husband's mother, who'd just come here from Jamaica, complained of pain – she was ignored and ended up having cancer of the ovaries and she died . . . OK, that's just one story of one black woman but everyone's got their own collection of horror tales but there are too many of them – from people I know and in my working life – to just dismiss it. I do worry that if anything were seriously wrong with me, which is a fantasy I carry around with me a lot, especially with my own mother dying when she was 37 and it's my 37th year – she had no warning signs of pain and just died – so it's an interesting one with me.

Obviously, for Angela the role of gender is inextricable from class and ethnicity. She also thought that the questionnaire and interview should encompass the role of religion as well. Even if people did not see themselves as practising or believing in religion, as a lapsed Catholic she felt that the effects were still pervasive with regard to beliefs about pain. With regard to gender, Angela continued to express strongly the same viewpoint as in the questionnaire; namely that women are able to endure more pain than men are. She thought that the socialisation of men and boys makes the expression of pain more difficult for them but that, generally, they receive better 'service'. She believed very strongly that this superior coping ability is double-edged, and arises through the position of women in the social hierarchy, cross-cut by other characteristics, especially their ethnicity and social class:

> I've got a friend who's a midwife at St George's and she was working with a Somalian woman and she was terrified to shout out in labour – it would be a disclaimer of her womanhood to actually give in to the pain – totally reinforced by the husband. But I'm not saying that's just particular to Somalis or black people because I know in a lot of working class, traditionally European or Irish/English places, women don't say they're in pain – I'm not like that!

Conclusions: towards a sociology of pain and gender

Pain is not for no reason – it's part of a natural course of events – if you don't understand how to live your life there will be pain if you do it wrongly – a kind of punishment. Just as the mind and feelings can affect the body – like anxiety – so the sort of body you've got affects the emotions, so it's both . . . F5

English, which can express the thoughts of Hamlet and the tragedy of Lear has no words for the shiver or the headache . . . the merest schoolgirl when she falls in love has Shakespeare or Keats to speak her mind for her but let a sufferer try to describe a pain in his head to a doctor and language at once runs dry. (Woolf 1967: 17)

In this final chapter the contribution of the research is evaluated within a context, which takes account of its potential theoretical, methodological, social, and policy and practice implications. Broadly, it is argued that exploring and understanding the relations between the 'nature' and 'culture' of pain on the one hand and the social construction of gender on the other, can inform a range of other understandings, including those related to health, illness, normalcy, theories of embodiment, knowledge, science and power. Understanding the relations between pain perceptions and gender also throws light on medical theory and practice, and beyond this more generally on the 'set' of cultural values concerning humankind and the environment.

A multi-method approach to pain perception exploring the use of visual imagery in data collection

Quantitative and qualitative methods were combined to avoid reinforcing the dominant positivistic paradigm on pain perception. In addition, an innovatory approach to 'tapping' pain beliefs was initiated by using visual imagery to elicit responses relating to the conceptualisation of pain. A series of visual images, collected from art galleries, was used to tap men's and women's perceptions of pain. The images show men, women and children in different types of pain and in varied social circumstances. The idea of using visual images in order to probe more deeply into beliefs and attitudes about pain emerged from an interest stimulated by Berger (1972) and others in the relationship between art and society. Although the impact of social thought on art history is clearly evident, from Marxist and feminist analyses to more recent post-structuralist critiques, reciprocal attempts to use art itself to enhance our understanding of social processes are still relatively underdeveloped within British and American sociology. The roots of this (sociological) neglect can be traced back to the equation of science with progress and the subsequent dichotomisation of intuition and logic, subjectivity and objectivity (Zolberg 1990). Given the increasing 'destabilisation' of these categories in social theory today, a sociology of the arts would seem an obvious next step. Certainly the twentieth century has heralded enormous changes in the understanding of art, both historically and culturally. These developments have, in turn, resulted in an extension of definitions of 'the arts' and 'high culture' beyond the realm of fine art and painting, to include photography, 'performance art' and, perhaps more controversially, the media.

The methodological basis for using visual images to tap pain perceptions in this research also followed the work of Finch (1987) and others who have employed the 'vignette' technique in sociological research. The approach was successful, in the sense that nobody refused to take part and all except two interviewees claimed to enjoy the exercise, some even claiming to find it therapeutic. Having revealed in some depth earlier in the interview their own 'pain stories', interviewees seemed to find it a relief to turn from the personal to a more public aspect, namely to something that was happening to someone else. A further advantage of using images is that this technique elicits an immediate response and does not necessarily require a high level of articulation, as can be the case with other interview procedures. Because the set of images is standardised, a high degree of consistency between different interviewers in data collection methods can be guaranteed. The visual image technique was used in this research in combination with others (self-administered questionnaires, in-depth interviews, 'accounts' of pain, literature reviews) to build up a sociological picture of the ways in which pain is perceived, conceptualised, measured and socially patterned beyond the narrow domain of clinical–medical and psychological meanings in which the study of pain has traditionally been located.

Concepts of pain

The research presented in this thesis aimed to initiate a significant sociological contribution to the area of pain perception. This field has been dominated by psychophysical research, premised on the Cartesian dualism dominating Western medicine, and the resulting parallel divides between mind/body and emotion/sensation, which have been shown to limit and restrict treatment and therapy. Following the dualistic mechanical model, the conceptualisation of pain has traditionally been informed by medicopsychological approaches, among which the gate-control theory has been foremost in emphasising the significance of psychosocial and cultural variables.

The dichotomies of art and science, intuition and logic, and subjectivity and objectivity have resonances with the qualitative/quantitative and feminine/masculine splits described in earlier chapters. The contribution of feminist sociologists, especially in the body of work around the medicalisation of childbirth, health and healing and childhood, has achieved some advances in transcending these dualisms and the current work takes the form of a parallel exercise for pain by locating it in a context that unites nature *and* culture.

The original gate-control theory expanded the scientific model in the 1960s and was revised further by Bates in 1987 to take account of cultural factors, including the following: attention given to pain stimuli or sensation; attitudes towards pain; prior pain experiences; social comparison and social learning processes within ethnocultural group situations. The findings from the present study would expand the model still further by adding other variables to this list. First, structural differentiation produced by gender, class, age and other forms of social stratification would be included. In addition, beliefs about pain join forces with attitudes and concepts derived from religious and spiritual world-views. Even though a

person may not practise and may consciously reject religion, most cultures
are shaped and moulded by external belief systems which affect and inform
their perceptions of illness and pain. In other words, we would end up
with a second edition of the revised model of the gate-control theory,
one that places as much emphasis on the sociocultural variables as it does
on the biological.

As Cornwell (1984) has demonstrated, 'lay' knowledge of health and
healing may be composed of 'common-sense' notions or superstitions,
as well as religious beliefs, and may conflict with scientific, rational and
technical perspectives, which regard them as irrelevant. However, these
beliefs remain highly pertinent to the individual, and have been demonstrated to affect treatment and outcomes of pain therapy (Williams and
Thorn 1989; Priel, Rabinowitz and Pels 1991). Prior pain experiences are
differentiated into physical, emotional, acute, chronic, treated, untreated,
etc. Specific pain stimuli not only provoke attention from the individual,
but are individually interpreted, and thus given 'subjective' meanings. A
significant factor here is how others perceive and respond to the individual
in pain. These factors all feed into how pain is perceived, experienced,
reacted to and expressed physically, mentally and emotionally.

Medical practice and social values

A more holistic understanding of pain is clearly relevant to medical
practice on a number of different levels. The inability of medicine to explain
experienced pain for which there is no 'demonstrable' pathological cause
has led to an increased emphasis on sociocultural variables. Using a
semiotic perspective may be especially valid for chronic pain syndromes,
where pain is symbolic of either inner or outer conflict. People in pain,
of whatever type, may need their pain 'validating' before they can cope
with it. Underlying such considerations, the 'faulty-machine' model of
embodiment does not provide an approach adequate to the task of understanding the subjective meanings of pain.

Aside from specific medical practice issues, there are implications
on a broader social level of new approaches to understanding pain.
Potentially serious implications stem from the separation of reason and
feeling, not only for medical practice, but for human culture in general.
Instead of the hopes of a new and better world, designed to end ignor-
ance and superstition, which Descartes envisaged would be based on
reason, the ultimate implications of rationality can be seen in a more
sinister light:

It was an idea that at first sparked off great hope and optimism in the West. Yet it was also a blind hope which was crushed forever in the madness of the sheer 'rationality' of Auschwitz, where the mathematical idea of a final solution bore witness to a terrible flaw in the philosophical foundations of modern Western civilisation. For it was there, in one of the most sophisticated of all Western nations, that men who were clearly rational were also clearly incapable of hearing the cries of human suffering. If Germany was the most scientific – that is – rational of all nations – and if it had the most advanced medicine in the Western world, it was nevertheless a medicine almost totally deaf to those cries. To believe, however, that such deafness was peculiarly German, or the result of an aberration in what has otherwise been an inexorable movement towards greater enlightenment, is to feed the very same disease that produced this human catastrophe in the first place.   (Lynch 1985: 309)

As the 20th century ended, genocide continued to be perpetrated across the globe. In turn, the need to understand by what perceptual process it is possible for one human being to stand beside another in agonising pain and not recognise it or care about it, or to even revel in the fact that that he or she may be inflicting that pain, is paramount. *The Body in Pain: The Making and Unmaking of the World* (Scarry 1988), a powerful linguistic analysis of the nature of pain, suggests that torture is an extreme event parallel to war in that the object of war is to kill people, whereas torture mimes the killing of people by inflicting pain. Scarry maintains that torture is an imitation of death, 'a sensory equivalent, substituting prolonged mock execution for execution' (1988: 27), and is made more frightening by its 'acting out' properties. By inflicting bodily pain, it destroys and replaces personal language with the objectification and 'deconstruction' of the body and the person. She also concludes that any investigation into the nature of pain must include philosophical consideration of the capacity of humans to inflict pain on both their own, and other, species. Radical feminists have argued that both torture and war can be regarded as essentially masculine phenomena, counterpoised to feminine ways of thinking, understanding and acting (see Belenky *et al.* 1986; Ruddick 1990). Contentious, essentialist and even bigoted this proposition may be, but this study suggests that a strongly held notion among men and women seems to be that to have a body capable of creating and producing life within itself somehow produces a predisposition to avoiding destruction. Perhaps what is really important is whether that predisposition is seen as biologically fixed or as open to cultural acquisition; however, it does also reinforce the importance of an approach to perceptions of pain that is sensitive to the social construction and operation of gender differences, but also interlinked with class, race and other social characteristics. These themes connect to each other, as well as to more fundamental philosophical issues.

Gender and pain

In the literature on pain perception, either gender is not seen as a variable of any significance, or females are thought to have lower thresholds than males. The focus on sex differences in thresholds and tolerance appears to be the *only* issue regarding gender and pain perception to have received any systematic attention.

Gender differences are most likely to be recorded in sensitivity to experimentally induced pain; a recent experiment which inflicted a noxious heat stimulus on a 'normal' sample of undergraduate men and women (Feine *et al.* 1991) concluded that there was a biological basis for the lower thresholds of the women. While asserting this finding as the most 'logical' explanation, the authors suggested that another interpretation could be that men delay responses more than women do. The issue of these observed sex differences reflecting response bias remains unresolved. In contrast to the psychophysical research conducted on thresholds and tolerance, the findings of the present study, which looks at beliefs about pain, reveal a superior coping attribution in favour of women. Very few men (17 per cent) or women (8 per cent) saw a superior male capacity in this area, whereas 66 per cent of women and 33 per cent of men thought that women coped better, and 25 per cent of men and 42 per cent of women thought that there were no differences. In other words, the perceived ability of women to cope with pain appears to be a heavily gendered notion.

In the explanations that participants gave in both the interviews and questionnaires for the present research, biological principles for these differences were cited along with broad sociocultural themes of *roles* and *socialisation* – both highly contested concepts. Both men and women believed that female hormonal and reproductive functioning and the role of motherhood equip girls and women with a 'natural' capacity to endure pain, whereas there is no such biological preparation for boys and men. Although it was felt that women were more likely to admit to being in pain and to seek help or treatment, their assigned social roles made it less possible for them to adopt the sick role and restrict their activities. Both sexes felt that it was culturally more acceptable for women to express pain. Childhood socialisation was thought to lead males and females to differ in their perception, evaluation and response to symptoms. Male socialisation was seen to actively discourage males from being allowed to express either physical or emotional pain. Such expression was seen as a state of 'abnormality', in contrast to the assumptions of 'naturalness' in females.

Assumptions of 'naturalness' about female pain-coping capacities are linked to structural social divisions by gender, particularly between public and private domains. Women have historically been more closely involved than men in the domestic sphere, and have therefore also been associated with the 'natural' world in the form of bodily (implying *lower* status) functions. Major features of this division are female biology, particularly menstruation and reproduction (see Martin 1987; Laws 1990) and the rearing of children, a 'social' role that is often ascribed biological status. By comparison, men are more involved in the public world of work and therefore 'higher' cultural and mental processes: 'It is no accident that "natural" facts about women, in the form of claims about biology are often used to justify social stratification based on gender' (Martin 1987: 17). Although similar cultural claims about minority groups are often presented as biological or 'natural' facts, those who make these claims may be able to separate themselves from those groups in a way that they can never hope to separate themselves from women, as 'not only do most of them have a woman raising the kids at home, all of them surely believe that their children are genetically related – connected by shared biological substance – to their wives as well as themselves. Flaws in women might seem to have implications for their own families . . .' (Martin 1987: 18).

This study is not concerned with trying to demonstrate women's superiority over men but to probe into why beliefs about pain are so gendered, and possible sociocultural explanations as to why women are thought to cope better with pain include the following: a greater readiness to report pain; a greater likelihood of acting upon symptoms and seeking support or help; women have more imagination about how it feels to be in pain or distress as a result of childhood socialisation which puts greater emphasis on caring for others; and finally, women's ontological security and sense of identity is less threatened by admitting to vulnerability in the form of pain than is the case for men, whose psychological structure of masculinity is predisposed to inhibit such revelations.

The attribution to men and women of different capacities for experiencing, expressing, understanding and responding to pain is linked to gender-differentiated socialisation processes. Here the work of theorists such as Chodorow (1978), Martin (1987) and Young (1990) draws attention to the ways in which the experience of embodiment may be fundamentally differentiated for male and female children by virtue of the gender-asymmetrical nuclear family system. Physical experience of the body is modified by the social categories through which it is known. Therefore all theories about its care, its lifespan, its abilities, its functions and its ability to withstand pain emanate from a culturally processed and located idea of the body. The experience of living in a body and being a gendered body in a hierarchically organised gender-differentiated world must have an impact on the ways in which different forms of pain are experienced and expressed.

Both female and male respondents in the interviews for the present study expressed the opinion that men (particularly those who are white, heterosexual and working in non-manual occupations) would take longer to admit to being in any type of pain or to seek treatment, but would be likely to receive more attention and be taken more seriously, whether by health workers or others around them – suggestions that are supported by studies of social characteristics and health service use, and by both historical and contemporary studies of the attitudes and behaviour of health professionals:

> It is of particular concern that in Britain a rigid set of monocultural social values congenial to men are urged on a plural, multiethnic society where women are disadvantaged and those who are not white, indigenous and middle-class especially so.
>
> (Mayall and Foster 1989: 2)

The role of emotions

A brief review of some of the literature on emotions in Chapter 2 pointed out the increasing interest of sociologists in the social functioning and cultural shaping of emotions. The findings of the present study demonstrate that emotions represent an important juncture between the mental and the physical, the mind and body, and the individual and society, and are especially relevant to the understanding of pain perception. Like emotions, perceptions of pain differ from other senses such as sight or vision because they do not require a particular environmental energy, and the identity of the individual and their personal belief and value systems appear to affect how pain is evaluated and interpreted. These factors also help to shape the expression of pain, which in turn reflects the individual's social context.

Pain is not always seen as negative, especially if it is acute, easily observable and the cause is established. Childbirth was described by respondents as 'productive' pain, and many people endorsed the notion of pain as having a *signal function* as being a sign of both biological and emotional health. Nevertheless, hierarchies of 'respectability' were ascribed to different types of pain. Emotions were only mentioned by 4 per cent of the questionnaire sample but the concept of 'emotional pain' was acknowledged by the entire interview sample.

There were gender differences in attitudes to this concept. For men especially, physical pain appeared to command more respect, legitimisation and sympathy and most were reluctant to see pain without a pathological cause as 'real' pain. Although the women in the sample did make distinctions between the physical and the emotional, they were more likely to describe their experiences in an holistic, integrated fashion.

Emotional pain was presented in terms of 'popular' concepts from humanistic psychology and psychoanalytic influences. Most of the respondents articulated the idea in some form that 'bottling up' feelings, and not being able to express emotional conflict or hurt, causes damage. However, the ability to be able to convey this distress in a 'safe' manner is seen as problematic, especially for men, as although on the one hand expressing emotion is seen to be positive and health-promoting, it is also double-edged. This is both in the sense of the vulnerability incurred by being seen to be 'weak' and the fear that is invoked by displays of emotion to others.

Lack of control, which severe pain of any origin may induce, is for many respondents a frightening thought and an experience to be avoided at all costs. However, 'real' acute pain with an easily demonstrable cause – for instance, injuries sustained through sport or battle – have a respectable status and demand instant attention. Less physically obvious 'hurts', especially emotional ones, are kept hidden for fears of personal vulnerability. Feeling safe enough to seek help thus depends on the social context.

The concept of 'emotion work' involves the management of emotions of the individual in order to conform to the demands of the particular social situation. These include both the subjective states and more public bodily displays. Hochschild (1983) has coined the phrase 'status shields' which are the socially distributed resources that people have for protecting their sense of self in differing social situations; here the private sphere is seen as more appropriate than the public. The tendency towards stoicism, the traditional British 'stiff upper lip', is often portrayed with pride, and may be continually instilled throughout childhood socialisation, especially for boys. However, negative consequences of the tendency to refrain from expressing ourselves can occur when symptoms are ignored, either by the sufferers themselves, or those who are supposed to be caring for them.

In health care (and no doubt in other areas of care) there is a tendency to label 'sick-role' behaviour as 'attention seeking' at best and malingering at worst, when in fact it may be the perceptions of the carers that need examining. Priel *et al.* (1991) demonstrate how the patient in pain needs to find a meaning for their symptoms, even if it is 'dysfunctional'. Without such a meaning, feelings of despair and isolation may develop. Explanations may be linked to deeply entrenched religious or spiritual beliefs, even if an individual does not follow any particular faith. The research carried out for this study shows that punishment and self-blame are common themes. Whereas they may seem inappropriate and even anti-therapeutic to the physician, these beliefs may preserve a sense of self-identity for the sufferer, in the face of impersonal rationality that medicine may impose.

Future research directions

In building on the methodology and the findings of the present study, future research needs to take a number of different directions. The common methodological starting point of these is the exploration of a new technique for evaluating pain which incorporates the systematising of the 'subjective' element omitted from traditional approaches. The methodological implications of the study clearly lie in developing the use of visual imagery more systematically, and with a larger, and different, sample of individuals. An obvious setting to examine further the productivity of this technique in exploring perceptions of pain would be among attendees at a pain clinic. (Most attendees have been referred to pain clinics because a 'pathological' cause for their symptoms could not be established.) Another development will be to compare the possible impact of professional training on perceptions of pain by applying the technique to health professionals as well as to individuals using pain clinics. In this work one objective would be to see if the number of images used could be reduced, and how the central issues stimulated by each could be controlled. Fine art and photographic images could be compared for their capacity to stimulate qualitatively different types of information regarding people's perceptions of pain. The visual imagery technique is also of clear relevance to the investigation of cultural differences in pain perceptions, and to the exploration of possible dissonances between the perceptions of health professionals and users of the health services.

From a theoretical point of view, the future development of research in this area will build on both the sociology of emotions and the sociology of embodiment as new domains and divisions of sociological labour. So far as advancing the understanding of pain as a gender-differentiated phenomenon is concerned, the sociological frameworks provided by feminist epistemology (Gilligan 1982; Belenky *et al.* 1986; Smith 1988; Grosz 1994; Battersby 1998) will be crucial. As well as being a medical(ised) phenomenon, pain is an everyday experience linking the subjective sense of self to the perceived 'objective' reality of the world and other people. In these aspects, the gendering of culture must affect and inform the experience of pain. It is thus this process that is likely to hold important clues to the well-documented picture of gender inequalities in health and illness. The experience of pain, which has formed the subject-matter of this study, constitutes an integral and hitherto poorly researched part of this picture. Its exploration does, moreover, both provide and demand the dissolution of the habit of dichotomous thinking which has impeded a unified understanding of cultural and biological inputs to health.

Adler, K. and Pointon, M. (1993) *The Body Imaged: The Human Form and Visual Culture since the Renaissance*, Cambridge: Cambridge University Press.

Ahmad, W. (1993) *'Race' and Health in Contemporary Britain*, Buckingham: Open University Press.

Alves, W. and Rossi, P. (1986) 'Who should get what? Fairness in the judgements of distribution of earnings', *American Journal of Sociology*, 84(3): 541–64.

Annandale, E. (1998) *The Sociology of Health and Medicine*, Oxford: Polity Press.

Anthias, F. and Yuval-Davis, N. (1983) 'Contextualising feminism: gender, ethnic and class divisions', *Feminist Review*, 15: 62–76.

Armstrong, D. (1983) *The Political Anatomy of the Body: Medical Knowledge in Britain in the Twentieth Century*, Cambridge: Cambridge University Press.

Armstrong, D. (1984) 'The patient's view', *Social Science and Medicine*, 18(9): 737–44.

Armstrong, D. (1995) 'The rise of surveillance medicine', *Sociology of Health and Illness*, 17(3): 393–404.

Arney, W. and Neill, J. (1982) 'The location of pain in natural childbirth: natural childbirth and the transformation of obstetrics', *Sociology of Health and Illness*, 4: 1–24.

Barrett, M. and Roberts, H. (1978) 'Doctors and their patients: the social control of women in general practice', in B. Smart and C. Smart (eds) *Women, Sexuality and Social Control*, London: Routledge and Kegan Paul.

Bates, M. (1987) 'Ethnicity and pain: a biocultural model', *Social Science and Medicine*, 24(1): 47–50.

Battersby, C. (1998) *The Phenomenal Woman*, Oxford: Polity Press.

Bayliss, R. (1998) 'Pain narratives', in T. Greenhalgh and B. Hurwitz (eds) *Narrative Based Medicine*, London: BMJ Books.

Bazanger, I. (1989) 'Pain: its experience and treatment', *Social Science and Medicine*, 29(3): 425–34.

de Beauvoir, S. (1959) *The Second Sex*, Harmondsworth: Penguin.

Beecher, H. (1959) *Measurement of Subjective Responses*, New York: Oxford University Press.

Belenky, M., Clinchy, B., Goldberger, N. and Tarule, J. (1986) *Women's Ways of Knowing*, New York: Basic Books.

Bendelow, G. (1993) 'Pain perceptions, emotions and gender', *Sociology of Health and Illness*, 15(3): 273–94.

Bendelow, G. (1996) 'The medical management of pain: views of chronic pain sufferers', in S.J. Williams and M. Calnan (eds) *Modern Medicine: Lay Perspectives and Experiences*, London: UCL Press.

Bendelow, G. and Williams, S.J. (1995a) 'Transcending the dualisms: towards a sociology of pain', *Sociology of Health and Illness*, 17(2): 139–65.

Bendelow, G. and Williams, S.J. (1995b) 'Pain and the mind–body dualism: a sociological approach', *Body and Society*, 1(2): 83–102.

Bendelow, G. and Williams, S.J. (1995c) 'Sociological approaches to pain', *Progress in Palliative Care*, 3(4): 2–7.

Bendelow, G. and Williams, S.J. (1996) 'The end of the road? Lay views on a pain relief clinic', *Social Science and Medicine*, 43(7): 1127–36.

Bendelow, G. and Williams, S.J. (1998a) *Emotions in Social Life: Social Theories and Contemporary Issues*, London: Routledge.

Bendelow, G. and Williams, S.J. (1998b) 'Natural for women, abnormal for men', in S. Nettleton and J. Watson (eds) *The Body in Everyday Life*, London: Routledge.

Berger, J. (1972) *Ways of Seeing*, Harmondsworth: Penguin.

Bhavnani, K. and Coulson, M. (1986) 'Transforming socialist-feminism: the challenge of racism', *Feminist Review*, 23: 81–91.

Blaxter, M. (1985) 'Self-definition of health status and consulting rates', *The Quarterly Journal of Social Affairs*, 7(2): 131–71.

Bloom, A. (1979) *Medicine for Nurses*, London: Churchill Livingstone.

Blumer, D. and Heilbronn, M. (1981) 'The pain-prone disorder: a clinical and psychological profile', *Psychosomatics*, 22: 395–402.

Bonica, J. (1953) *The Management of Pain*, Philadelphia: Lea & Febiger.

Bonner, R., Goodman, L., Allen, R., James, L. and King, C. (1992) (eds) *Imaging Women: Culture Representations and Gender*, Cambridge: Polity Press.

Bordo, S. (1986) 'The Cartesian masculinazation of thought', *Signs*, 11(3): 439–57.

Boring, E. (1942) *Sensation and Perception in the History of Experimental Psychology*, New York: Appleton Century Croft.

Bourdieu, P. (1980) *Questions de Sociologie*, Paris: Editions de Minuit.

Bourdieu, P., Dabel, A. and Schnapper, D. (1990) *The Logic of Practice*, Cambridge: Polity Press.

Brannen, J. (1989) *Combining Quantitative and Qualitative Research*, paper for Conference on Research Methods, Thomas Coram Research Unit, Institute of Education.

Brown, G. (1996) 'Life events, loss and depressive disorders', in T. Heller, J. Reynolds, R. Gomm, R. Muston and S. Pattison (eds) *Mental Health Matters*, Milton Keynes: Open University Press.

Brown, G. and Harris, T. (1978) *Social Origins of Depression*, London: Tavistock.

Bryan, B., Dadzie, S. and Scarfe, S. (1985) *The Heart of the Race: Black Women's Lives in Britain*, London: Virago.

Bryman, A. (1988) *Quantity and Quality in Social Research*, London: Unwin Hyman.

Burgess, R. (ed.) (1986) *Key Variables in Social Investigation*, London: Routledge.

Bury, M. (1982) 'Chronic illness as biographical disruption', *Sociology of Health and Illness*, 1(2): 167–82.

Busfield, J. (1988) 'Mental illness as a social product or social construction: a contradiction in feminists' arguments?', *Sociology of Health and Illness*, 10(4): 521–42.

Busfield, J. (1998) *Men, Women and Madness*, London: Macmillan.

Buss, A. (1975) 'The emerging field of the sociology of psychological knowledge', *American Psychologist*, 37, October: 988–1000.

Butler, J. (1993) *Body Matters: The Discursive Limits of Sex*, London: Routledge.

Cancian, F. (1987) *Love in America*, Cambridge: Cambridge University Press.

Carmichael, K. (1985) 'The creative use of pain in society', in R. Terrington (ed.) *Towards a Whole Society*, London: Richmond Fellowship Press.

Cartwright, A. (1984) 'Monitoring maternity services by postal questionnaires to mothers', *Health Trends*, 19: 19–20.

Chodorow, N. (1978) *The Reproduction of Mothering*, Berkeley: University of California Press.

Clarke, J. (1983) 'Sexism, feminism and medicalism: a decade review of the literature on gender and illness', *Sociology of Health and Illness*, 5(1): 62–82.

Cochrane, A. (1995) *Effectiveness and Efficiency in Health and Disease: A Reader*, Oxford: Oxford University Press.

Connell, R. (1979) 'The concept of "role" and what to do with it', *Australian and New Zealand Journal of Sociology*, 15: 7–17.

Connell, R. (1985) 'Theorising gender', *Sociology*, 19(2): 260–73.

Cornwell, J. (1984) *Hard-Earned Lives: Accounts of Health and Illness from East London*, London: Tavistock.

Coward, R. (1989) *The Whole Truth: The Myth of Alternative Health*, London: Faber & Faber.

Craig, K. (1984) 'Emotional aspects of pain', in P. Wall and R. Melzack (eds) *A Textbook of Pain*, London: Churchill Livingstone.

Crooke, J., Rideout, E. and Browne, G. (1984) 'The prevalence of pain complaints in a general population', *Pain*, 18: 299–314.

Csordas, T.J. (ed.) (1994) *Embodiment and Experience: The Existential Ground of Culture and Self*, Cambridge: Cambridge University Press.

Darwin, C. (1895/1955) *The Expression of Emotion in Man and Animals*, New York: Philosophical Library.

Davitz, J. (1969) *The Language of Emotion*, New York: Academic Press.

Descartes, R. (1664/1972) *The Treatise of Man*, Cambridge, MA· Harvard University Press.

Dewey, J. (1922) *Human Nature and Conduct: An Introduction to Social Psychology*, New York: Holt.

Dougher, M., Goldstein, D. and Leigh, K. (1987) 'Induced anxiety and pain', *Journal of Anxiety Disorders*, 1(3): 259–64.

Doyal, L. and Pennell, I. (1979) *The Political Economy of Health*, London: Pluto Press.

Dubreuil, D. and Kohn, P. (1986) 'Reactivity and response to pain', *Personality and Individual Differences*, 7: 907–9.

Durkheim, E. (1897) *Suicide: A Study in Sociology*, London: Routledge & Kegan Paul.

Duster, T. and Garrett, K. (1987) *Cultural Perspectives on Biological Knowledge*, New Jersey: Ablex.

Ecclestone, C. (1997) 'Patients and professionals' understandings of the causes of chronic pain: blame, reponsibility, and identity protection', *Social Science and Medicine*, 45(5): 699–709.

Ehrenreich, B. and English, D. (1974) *For Her Own Good: 150 years of Expert Advice to Women*, London: Pluto Press.

Elton, D., Quarry, P., Burrows, G. and Stanley, G. (1978) 'The Melbourne pain apperception film', *Melbourne Psychology Reports*, 45: 1–12.

Elton, D., Stanley, G. and Burrows, G. (1983) *Psychological Control of Pain*, Australia: Grune & Stratton.

Engel, G. (1958) 'Psychogenic pain and the pain prone patient', *American Journal of Medicine*, 26: 899–918.

Eysenck, H.J. (1956) 'The questionnaire measurement of neuroticism and extraversion', *Rivista di Piscologia*, 54: 113–40.

Falk, P. (1994) *The Consuming Body*, London: Sage.

Featherstone, M., Hepworth, M. and Turner, B. (eds) (1991) *The Body: Social Process and Cultural Theory*, London, Newbury Park, CA and New Delhi: Sage.

Feine, J., Bushnell, M., Miron, D. and Duncan, G. (1991) 'Sex differences in the perception of noxious heat stimuli', *Pain*, 44(3): 255–63.

Finch, J. (1984) ' "It's good to have someone to talk to": the ethics and politics of interviewing women', in C. Bell and H. Roberts (eds) *Social Researching*, London: Routledge & Kegan Paul.

Finch, J. (1987) 'Research note: the vignette technique in survey research', *Sociology*, 21(1): 105–14.

Finkler, K. (1994) *Women in Pain*, Philadelphia: University of Pennsylvania Press.

Fischer, E. (1964) *The Necessity of Art*, Penguin: Harmondsworth.

Foucault, M. (1973) *The Birth of the Clinic: An Archaeology of Medical Practice*, London: Tavistock.

Fox, B. (1981) 'Psychosocial factors and the immune system in human cancer', in R. Ader (ed.) *Psychoneuroimmunology*, New York: Academic Press.

Frank, A. (1995) *The Wounded Storyteller: Body Illness and Ethics*, Chicago and London: University of Chicago Press.

Freud, S. (1911) 'Formulations on two principles of mental functioning', in J. Strachey (ed.) *Essays of Freud*, Standard edn vol. 12, London: Hogarth Press.

Freund, P. (1990) 'The expressive body: a common ground for the sociology of emotions and health and illness', *Sociology of Health and Illness*, 12(4): 452–77.

Friedson, E. (1970) *The Profession of Medicine*, New York: Dodd Mead.

Fyfe, G. and Law, J. (1988) *Picturing Power: Visual Depictions and Social Relations*, London: Routledge.

Garrett, K. (1984) 'Women's reproductive rhythms: the nature/nurture conundrum', in T. Duster and K. Garrett (eds) *Cultural Perspectives on Biological Knowledge*, New Jersey: Ablex.

Gehring, E. (1932) 'Painful women', *Journal of the Maine Medical Association*, 23(7): 139–43.

Gentry, W., Stows, W. and Thomes, M. (1974) 'Chronic low back pain: a psychological profile', *Psychosomatics*, 15: 174–7.

Gerth, H. and Wright Mills, C. (1964) *Character and Social Structure: The Psychology of Social Institutions*, New York: Harcourt, Brace, Jovanovich.

Gilligan, C. (1982) *In a Different Voice: Psychological Theory and Women's Development*, Cambridge, MA: Harvard University Press.

Glaser, J. and Glaser, R. (1986) 'Psychological influences on immunity', *Psychosomatics*, 27: 621–4.

Goffman, E. (1959) *The Presentation of Everyday Life*, New York: Doubleday Anchor.

Goffman, E. (1979) *Gender Advertisements*, London: Macmillan.

Good, M., Brodwin, B., Good, B. and Kleinman, A. (1992) *Pain as Human Experience: An Anthropological Perspective*, Berkeley, CA and London: University of California Press.

Gove, W. (1978) 'Sex differences in mental illness among adult men and women', *Social Science and Medicine*, 12B: 187–98.

Gove, W. and Hughes, M. (1979) 'Possible causes of the apparent sex differences in physical differences in physical health: an empirical investigation', *American Sociological Review*, 44: 126–46.

Graham, H. (1983) 'Do her answers fit his questions? Women and the survey method', in E. Garmanikow, D. Morgan, J. Purvis and D. Taylorson (eds) *The Public and the Private*, London: Heinemann Educational.

Greene, J. (1990) 'Perception', in I. Roth (ed) *Introduction to Psychology*, Milton Keynes: Open University Press.

Greenhalgh, T. (1998) 'Narrative based medicine in an evidence based world', in T. Greenhalgh and B. Hurwitz, *Narrative Based Medicine*, London: BMJ Books.

Greenhalgh, T. and Hurwitz, B. (1998) *Narrative Based Medicine*, London: BMJ Books.

Gregory, R. (1972) *Eye and Brain*, London: Weidenfeld & Nicholson.

Grosz, E. (1994) *Volatile Bodies: Toward a Corporeal Feminism*, Bloomington and Indianapolis: Indiana University Press.

Harding, S. (1987) *Feminism and Methodology: Social Science Issues*, Milton Keynes: Open University Press.

Hardy, J., Woolf, H. and Goddell, H. (1968) *Pain Sensations and Reactions*, New York: Hafner.

Harre, R. and Secord, P. (1972) *The Explanation of Social Behaviour*, Oxford: Basil Blackwell.

Hart, N. (1985) *The Sociology of Health and Illness*, Ormskirk: Causeway.

Head, H. (1920) *Studies in Neurology*, London: Routledge & Kegan Paul.

Helkimo, M. (1976) 'Epidemiological surveys of dysfunction of the masticatory system', *Oral Science Review*, 7: 54–69.

Helman, C. (1979) *Culture, Health and Illness: An Introduction for Health Professionals*, Bristol: John Wright.

Hochschild, A. (1979) 'Emotion work, feeling rules and social structure', *American Journal of Sociology*, 85: 551–75.

Hochschild, A. (1983) *The Managed Heart: The Commercialization of Human Feeling*, Berkeley: University of California Press.

Hochschild, A. (1998) 'Emotions as a way of seeing: the case of love', in G. Bendelow and S.J. Williams (eds) *Emotions in Social Life: Social Theories and Contemporary Issues*, London: Routledge.

Hockey, J. and James, A. (1993) *Growing Up and Growing Old*, London: Sage.

Humphreys, C. and Elford, J. (1990) 'Sociology and epidemiology in medical education: interpreting the student's response', *Medical Education*, 24: 171–7.

Hydén, L. (1997) 'Illness and narrative', *Sociology of Health and Illness*, 19(1): 48–69.

Illich, I. (1976) *Limits to Medicine: Medical Nemesis – the Expropriation of Health*, London: Marion Boyars.

James, N. and Gabe, J. (1996) *Health and the Sociology of Emotions*, Oxford: Blackwell.

James, A., Jenks, C. and Prout, A. (1998) *Theorizing Childhood*, Cambridge: Polity Press.

Jarman, B. (1983) 'Identifying underprivileged areas', *BMJ*, 286: 1705–9.

Keefe, O. (1986) 'Depression, pain and pain behaviour', *Journal of Consulting and Clinical Psychology*, 54(5): 665–9.

Keele, K. (1957) *Anatomies of Pain*, Milton Keynes: Open University Press.

Kelleher, D. and Hillier, S. (1996) *Researching Cultural Differences in Health*, London: Routledge.

Kierkegaard, S. (1847/1962) *Works of Love: Some Christian Reflections in the Form of Discourses*, London: Collins.

Klein, V. (1946) *The Feminine Character: History of an Ideology*, London: Routledge & Kegan Paul.

Kleinman, A. (1988) *The Illness Narratives: Suffering, Healing and the Human Condition*, New York: Basic Books.

von Korff, M., Dworkin, S., Le Resche, L. and Kruger, A. (1988) 'An epidemiologic comparison of pain complaints', *Pain*, 32: 173–83.

Kortaba, J. (1977) 'Existential sociology', in S. McNall (ed.) *Theoretical Perspectives in Sociology*, New York: St Martin's Press.

Kortaba, J. (1983) *Chronic Pain: Its Social Dimensions*, Beverly Hills, CA: Sage.

Lawlis, G., Achterberg, J., Kenner, L. and Kopetz, K. (1984) 'Ethnic and sex differences in response to clinical and induced pain in chronic spinal pain patients', *Spine*, 9: 751–4.

Laws, S. (1990) *Issues of Blood: The Politics of Menstruation*, London: Macmillan.

Lee, R. and Renzetti, C. (1990) 'Researching sensitive topics: an overview and introduction', *American Behavioral Scientist*, 33(5): 510–28.

Levine, F. and de Simone, L. (1991) 'The effects of experimenter gender on pain report in male and female subjects', *Pain*, 44: 69–72.

Lippard, L. (1976) *From the Center: Feminist Essays on Women's Art*, New York: Thames & Hudson.

Lomas Cook, F. (1979) *Who Should Be Helped? Public Support for Social Services*, Beverly Hills, CA: Sage.

Lynch, J. (1977) *The Broken Heart: The Medical Consequences of Loneliness*, New York: Basic Books.

Lynch, J. (1985) *The Language of the Heart: The Human Body in Dialogue*, New York: Basic Books.

MacIntyre, A. (1982) *After Virtue*, Notre Dame, IN: University of Notre Dame Press.

Mann, R. (ed.) (1988) *A History of the Management of Pain: From Early Principles to Present Practice*, Carnforth: Parthenon.

Margolis, R., Zinny, G., Miller, D. and Taylor, J. (1984) 'Internists and the chronic pain patient', *Pain*, 20: 151–6.

Marshall, R. (1894) *Pain, Pleasure and Aesthetics*, London: Macmillan.

Martin, E. (1987) *The Woman in the Body*, Milton Keynes: Open University Press.

Martin, E. (1994) *Flexible Bodies*, Boston, MA: Beacon Press.

Marx, K. (1867/1978) *Capital*, Vol. 1, Chicago: Charles H. Kerr.

Maslow, A.H. (1987) *Motivation and Personality*, New York: Harper & Row (3rd edn).

Mayall, B. (1996) *Children, Health and the Social Order*, Buckingham: Oxford University Press.

Mayall, B. and Foster, M. (1989) *Living with Children: Working for Children*, London: Heinemann Nursing.

McKeown, T. (1977) *The Role of Medicine: Dream, Mirage or Nemesis?*, Oxford: Open University Press.

Melzack, R. (1975) 'The McGill pain questionnaire: major properties and scoring methods', *Pain*, 1a: 277–99.

Melzack, R. and Wall, P. (1965) 'Pain mechanisms: a new theory', *Science*, 150: 971–9.

Melzack, R. and Wall, P. (1988) *The Challenge of Pain*, Harmondsworth: Penguin.

Merskey, H. (1965) 'The characteristics of persistent pain in psychological illness', *Journal of Psychosomatic Research*, 9: 291–8.

Merskey, H. and Spear, E.G. (1967) *Pain: Psychological and Psychiatric Aspects*, London: Balliere, Tindall & Cassall.

Mishler, H. (1984) *The Discourse of Medicine*, Cambridge: Cambridge University Press.

Mitchell, J. (1975) *Psychoanalysis and Feminism*, Harmondsworth: Penguin.

Money, J. (1965) *Psychosexual Differentiation in Sex Research: New Developments*, New York: Holt, Rinehart & Winston.

de Montaigne (1592/1959) *In Defense of Raymond Sebend*, trans. A. Beattie, New York: Unger.

Morris, D. (1991) *The Culture of Pain*, Berkeley, CA and London: University of California Press.

Morris, D. (1998) *Illness and Culture in the Postmodern Age*, Berkeley, CA and London: University of California Press.

Nathanson, C. (1980) 'Social roles and health status among women: the significance of employment', *Social Science and Medicine*, 14A: 463–71.

Navarro, V. (1980) 'The labour process and health: a historical materialist interpretation', *International Journal of Health Services*, 12: 5–29.

Neisser, V. (1976) *Cognition and Reality*, San Francisco: Freeman.

Neri, M. and Agazzani, E. (1984) 'Aging and right–left asymmetry in experimental pain measurement', *Pain*, 19: 43–8.

Nettleton, S. (1989) 'Power and pain: the location of pain and fear in dentistry and the creation of a dental subject', *Social Science and Medicine*, 29(10): 1183–90.

Nettleton, S. and Watson, J. (1998) *The Body in Everyday Life*, London and New York: Routledge.

Newton, T. (1998) 'The sociogenesis of emotion: a historical sociology?', in G. Bendelow and S.J. Williams (eds) *Emotions in Social Life: Social Theories and Contemporary Issues*, London: Routledge.

Nochlin, L. (1989) *Women, Art and Power*, London: HarperCollins.

Notermans, S. and Tophoff, M. (1967) 'Sex differences in pain tolerance and pain apperception', *Psychiatria, Neurologia, Neurochirurgia: Journal of the Netherlands Society of Psychiatry and Neurology*, 70: 23–9.

Nurofen (1989) *Pain Relief Study*, London: Kings Fund.

Oakley, A. (1972) *Sex Gender and Society*, London: Maurice Temple Smith.

Oakley, A. (1980) *Women Confined: Towards a Sociology of Childbirth*, Oxford: Martin Robertson.

Oakley, A. (1981) 'Interviewing women: a contradiction in terms', in H. Roberts (ed.) *Doing Feminist Research*, London: Routledge & Kegan Paul.

Oakley, A. (1984) *The Captured Womb: A History of the Medical Care of Pregnant Women*, Oxford: Basil Blackwell.

Oakley, A. (1989) 'Who's afraid of the randomised controlled trial?', in H. Roberts (ed.) *Women's Health Counts*, London: Routledge & Kegan Paul.

Oakley, A. (1992) *Social Support and Motherhood*, Oxford: Basil Blackwell.

Oakley, A. (1998) 'Gender, methodology and people's ways of knowing: some problems with feminism and the paradigm debate in social science', *Sociology*, 32(4): 707–33.

Oakley, A., Rajan, L. and Robertson, P. (1990) 'A comparison of different sources of information about pregnancy and childbirth', *Journal of Biosocial Science*, 22: 477–87.

Oliver, M. (1996) *Understanding Disability: From Theory to Practice*, London: Macmillan.

OPCS (1994) *General Household Survey*, London: HMSO.

Otto, M. and Dougher, M. (1985) 'Sex differences and personality factors in responsivity to pain', *Perceptual and Motor Skills*, 61: 383–90.

Parsons, T. (1942) 'Age and sex in the social structure of the U.S.', in *Essays in Sociological Theory*, New York: Free Press.

Parsons, T. (1951) *The Social System*, Chicago: Free Press.

Parsons, T. and Bales, R. (1953) *Family, Socialisation and Interaction Process*, London: Routledge & Kegan Paul.

Petersen, A. and Bunton, R. (1997) *Foucault, Health and Medicine*, London: Routledge.

Petherbridge, D. and Jordanova, L. (1997) *The Quick and the Dead: Artists and Anatomy*, London: South Bank Centre.

Petrovich, D.V. (1957) 'The pain apperception test: a preliminary report', *Journal of Psychology*, 44: 339–46.

Phoenix, A. (1991) *Teenage Mothers?*, Cambridge: Polity Press.

Pitts, M. and Phillips, K. (1990) *The Psychology of Health: An Introduction*, London: Routledge & Kegan Paul.

Pollock, G. (1982) 'Vision, voice and power: feminist art history and Marxism', *Block*, 6: 6–9.

Popay, J. and Bartley, M. (1989) 'Work roles and health of men and women', unpublished paper for Health Advisory Group, Thomas Coram Research Unit, University of London.

Popkin, A. (1979) 'The personal is political: the women's liberation movement', in D. Cluster (ed.) *They Should Have Served That Cup of Coffee*, Boston, MA: South End Press.

Priel, B., Rabinowitz, B. and Pels, R. (1991) 'A semiotic perspective on chronic pain: implications for the interaction between patient and physician', *British Journal of Medical Psychology*, 64: 65–71.

Procacci, P. and Maresca, M. (1985) 'A philological study on some words containing pain', *Pain*, 22: 201–3.

Reissman, C.K. (1989) 'Women and medicalisation: a new perspective', in P. Brown (ed.) *Perpectives in Medical Sociology*, Belmont, CA: Wadsworth.

Revolutionary Health Committee of Hunan Province (1978) *A Barefoot Doctor's Manual*, London: Routledge & Kegan Paul.

Ribbens, J. and Edwards, R. (1997) *Feminist Dilemmas in Qualitative Research*, London: Sage.

Ricoeur, P. (1984) *Time and Narrative*, Vol. 1, Chicago: Chicago University Press.

Roberts, H. (ed.) (1981) *Women, Health and Reproduction*, London: Routledge & Kegan Paul.

Roberts, H. (1985) *The Patient Patients: Women and their Doctors*, London: Pandora.

Rose, S., Lewontin, R. and Leonikamen, E. (1984) *Not in Our Genes: Biology, Ideology and Human Nature*, Harmondsworth: Penguin.

Ruddick, S. (1990) *Maternal Thinking*, London: Women's Press.

Ryle, G. (1949) *The Concept of Mind*, Harmondsworth: Penguin.

Saunders, C. (1976) 'Care of the dying', *Nursing Times*, 72: 3–24.

Scarry, E. (1988) *The Body in Pain: The Making and Unmaking of the World*, Oxford: Oxford University Press.

Sedgwick, P. (1973) *Psychopolitics*, London: Pluto Press.

Shilling, C. (1993) *The Body in Social Theory*, London: Sage.

Shoben, E. and Borland, L. (1954) 'An empirical study of the aetiology of dental fears', *Journal of Clinical Psychology*, 10: 171–4.

Smith, D. (1975) 'The statistics of mental illness: what they will not tell us about women and why', in D. Smith and S. David (eds) *Women Look at Psychiatry*, Vancouver: Press Gang.

Smith, D. (1987) 'Woman's place in man's life cycle', in S. Harding (ed.) *Feminism and Methodology*, Milton Keynes: Open University Press.

Smith, D. (1988) *The Everyday World as Problematic*, Milton Keynes: Open University Press.

Solouriac, A., Cahn, J. and Charpentier, J. (eds) (1968) *Pain*, London: Academic Press.

Squibb, for Bristol-Myers (1987) *Survey of Mild–Moderate Pain amongst North American Men and Women*, British Library.

Stacey, M. (1981) 'The division of labour revisited, or overcoming the two Adams', in P. Abrams and R. Deem (eds) *Practice and Progress: British Sociology 1950–1980*, London: Allen & Unwin.

Stacey, M. (1988) *The Sociology of Health and Healing: A Textbook*, London: Unwin Hyman.

Strong, P. (1979) 'Sociological imperialism and the profession of medicine: a critical examination of the thesis of medical imperialism', *Social Science and Medicine*, 13A: 199–215.

Taylor, C. (1989) *Sources of the Self: The making of Modern Identity*, Cambridge: Cambridge University Press.

Taylor, J.A. (1953) 'Personality scale of manifest anxiety', *Journal of Abnormal and Social Psychology*, 48: 285–90.

Thewelweit, K. (1987/1989) *Male Fantasies*, Cambridge: Polity Press.

Tillich, P. (1968) *Systematic Theology*, Welwyn: Nisbet.

Tonnies, S. (1963) *Community and Society* (ed. and trans. Chas Loonis), New York: Harper Textbooks.

Townend, P., Davidson, N. and Whitehead, M. (1988) *Inequalities in Health: The Black Report and the Health Divide*, Harmondsworth: Penguin.

Turner, B. (1989) 'The body in sociology: Plenary for B.S.A. Medical Sociology Conference Manchester', *Medical Sociology News*, 15(1): 9–15.

Turner, B. (1991) 'Recent developments in the theory of the body', in M. Featherstone, M. Hepworth and B. Turner (eds) *The Body: Social Process and Cultural Theory*, London, Newbury Park, CA and New Delhi: Sage.

Turner, B. (1992) *Regulating Bodies: Essays in Medical Sociology*, London: Routledge.

Turner, B. (1995) *Medical Power and Social Knowledge*, London: Sage.

Tyler, L. (1965) *The Psychology of Human Differences*, New York: Appleton Century Croft.

Tyrer, S. (1986) 'Learned pain behaviour', *British Medical Journal*, 292: 1.

Verbrugge, L. (1985) 'Gender and health: an update on hypothesis and evidence', *Journal of Health and Social Behavior*, 26: 156–82.

Verbrugge, L. (1990) 'Pathways of health and disease', in R. Apple (ed.) *Women, Health and Medicine in America: A Historical Handbook*, New York: Garland.

Verbrugge, L. and Wingard, D. (1987) 'Sex differentials in health and mortality', *Women and Health Review*, 12(2): 103–43.

Vrancken, M. (1989) 'Schools of thought on pain', *Social Science and Medicine*, 29(3): 435–44.

Wagner, M. (1982) 'Getting the health out of people's daily lives', *The Lancet*, November: 1207–8.

Waldron, I. (1983) 'Sex differences in illness incidence, prognosis and mortality: issues and evidence', *Social Science and Medicine*, 17: 1107–23.

Wall, P. (1999) *Pain: The Science of Suffering*, London: Weidenfeld & Nicolson.

Wall, P. and Melzack, R. (1984) *A Textbook of Pain*, Edinburgh: Churchill Livingstone.

Wex, M. (1979) *Let's Take Back Our Space: 'Female' and 'Male' Body Language as a Result of Patriarchal Structure*, trans. J. Albert, Munich: Frauenliteraturverlag Hermine Hes.

Wilkins, R. (1991) 'Taking it personally: emotional processes in sociological research towards a sophisticated sensibility', paper for B.S.A. Conference 'Health and Society', Manchester University.

Williams, D. and Thorn, B. (1989) 'An empirical assessment of pain beliefs', *Pain*, 36: 351–8.

Williams, G. (1984) 'The genesis of chronic illness: narrative reconstruction', *Sociology of Health and Illness*, 6: 175–200.

Williams, S. (forthcoming) *Emotion and Social Theory*, London: Sage.

Williams, S.J. and Bendelow, G. (1998a) *The Lived Body: Sociological Themes, Embodied Issues*, London: Routledge.

Williams, S.J. and Bendelow, G. (1998b) 'In search of the "missing" body: pain, suffering and the (post)modern condition', in G. Scambler and P. Higgs (eds) *Modernity, Medicine and Health*, London: Routledge.

Williamson, J. (1978) *Decoding Advertisements: Ideology and Meaning in Advertising*, London: Marion Boyars.

Wittgenstein, L. (1921/1962) *Tractacus Logicophilosophicus*, London: Routledge & Kegan Paul.

Wolff, J. (1975) *Hermeneutic Philosophy and the Sociology of Art*, Routledge & Kegan Paul.

Wolff, J. (1985) *The Social Production of Art*, London: Routledge & Kegan Paul.

Woodrow, K., Friedman, G., Siegelaub, A. and Cohen, M. (1972) 'Pain tolerance: differences according to age, sex and race', *Psychosomatic Medicine*, 34: 548–55.

Woolf, V. (1967) 'On being ill', in *Collected Essays*, Vol. 4, New York: Harcourt.

World Health Organisation (1983) *Regional Strategy for Europe*, EWR/rc30/8, Geneva.

Wright Mills, C. (1959) *The Sociological Imagination*, Harmondsworth: Penguin.

Young, I. (1990) *Throwing Like a Girl and Other Essays in Feminist Philosophy and Social Theory*, Bloomington and Indianapolis: Indiana University Press.

Zborowski, M. (1952) 'Cultural components in response to pain', *Journal of Social Issues*, 8: 16–30.

Zola, I. (1966) 'Culture and symptoms: an analysis of patients' presenting complaints', *American Sociological Review*, 31: 615–30.

Zola, I. (1977) 'Medicine as an institution of social control', *Sociological Review*, 20: 487.

Zolberg, V. (1990) *Constructing a Sociology of the Arts*, Cambridge: Cambridge University Press.

index